To
/

Calum + Margaret

With Love

Jeremy -

6/9/18

A
LISTENING
DOCTOR

A
LISTENING
DOCTOR

JEREMY BENDING

QUARTET BOOKS

First published in 2018 by Quartet Books Limited
A member of the Namara Group
27 Goodge Street, London, W1T 2LD

A catalogue record for this book is available from the British Library

ISBN 9780704374539

Typeset by Tetragon, London
Printed and bound in Great Britain by TJ International Ltd, Padstow, Cornwall

To my wife Jan and our four children,
who had to put up with all of this.

And, not least, to my patients: I always
enjoyed listening to them and I hope
they found my listening helpful.

Contents

Whenever I was asked at a party,
'What exactly does a "physician" *do*?' I would reply,
'I don't cut anything out, or stick anything in.
I'm a *listening* doctor.'

INTRODUCTION

'That Doctor Listens to Me'

THE ROLE OF THE 'PHYSICIAN' IN THE ENGLISH SENSE
of the word – as opposed to the American, which is inter-
changeable with the word doctor, and any doctor at that
– is poorly understood. And by this, I mean that it is poorly
understood not only by patients and the community at
large, but also by hospital managers, politicians and even –
perhaps most critically – by the UK Department of Health
itself. A consultant physician would be called an internist or
a specialist in internal medicine in the USA. In the UK the
name consultant physician is given to all consultants who
are specialists in medical disciplines (as opposed to surgical
disciplines), whatever their specialty (e.g. cardiology, gastro-
enterology, respiratory medicine and neurology, to name a
few). My specialty was in diabetes (the lifelong condition in
which the body loses its ability to control blood glucose –
sugar – levels) and endocrinology (diseases of the hormone
glands other than the pancreas). Most of my time as a specialist in diabetes and endocrinology was spent listening to
patients. I did not 'cut anything out' or 'stick anything in'.
I was a 'listening doctor'.

The fact of the matter is that our present-day society is focussed on 'doing' to the detriment of all else. With the increased emphasis on the short-term planning of health economics and strategy – which is great for measuring 'events', such as the number of hernia repairs or varicose vein operations performed by a given surgeon or National Health Service trust – the place of the listening doctor in the diagnostic and healing process is so poorly understood by today's society as to be virtually non-existent. Those responsible for making management decisions, both at local hospital level and national NHS planning level, are more or less tuned in to the fact that the 'craft' specialties – i.e. largely the surgical disciplines – need time for training if a doctor is to become proficient in them. If nothing else, this appreciation comes out of the, somewhat cynical, acceptance that 'if we don't train surgeons adequately they will make mistakes which will ultimately cost the NHS huge sums in compensation payments'. And they will.

Having said this, it is also the case that the Royal College of Surgeons is rightly concerned about the amount of hours and the number of procedures which a surgeon in training receives in his or her specialist registrar training years. Stories abound of young surgeons who have been appointed to consultant surgeon posts having to undergo further periods of training in order for them to safely fly solo. The metaphor is apt: we know very well that airline pilots have to undergo rigorous training and many prescribed hours of supervised flying before they are able to take control of the jet we are flying off on holiday in. Usually through no fault of their own, these young surgeons have not received an adequate amount of experience during their training years to enable them to reach the desired standard in their surgical specialty.

So what is the situation in the non-craft (i.e. non-practical procedure) world of the listening doctor? The fact is that training to become a consultant physician requires as much time as it does for those learning to 'stick things in' and 'cut things out'. The art and skills, as well as the science, required by a consultant physician need just as much time to be taught and absorbed as does the training of a surgeon in practical surgical procedures. And the role of the fully trained listening doctor is just as crucial to the quality and effectiveness of our Health Service. It's just that it remains misunderstood and therefore very often ignored.

If the role of the listening doctor is something quite outside the boundaries of understanding for those in a managerial, health economy or political sphere, it also happens to be outside the understanding of much of the general public, who are often already convinced about what they need from their doctor, of any species, before they get to see him or her. Patients generally go to see a doctor to 'have things put right' with their health and to 'get things done'. People may be surprised to learn that, quite simply, physicians act as the listeners to the pathology of illness and are the chroniclers of disease. We often do not offer to 'stick anything in', or to 'cut anything out'. We are sorry if this leaves our patients disappointed. But we do hope to have a beneficial therapeutic effect.

On the other hand, it is quite clear that people do appreciate being listened to, as opposed to being talked at, or being ignored. How often have we heard someone say, 'I like that doctor, he takes time to listen to me'?

I

Listening Acutely

IT IS CLEAR FROM THE START, THEREFORE, THAT PEOPLE do not understand what it is that consultant physicians do. 'What do you do for a living?' someone might ask me.

'I'm a doctor,' I would say.

'Oh yes,' would be the reply, 'are you a GP?'

'No,' I would say, 'a hospital specialist.'

Immediately, the assumption: 'So you're a surgeon?'

The response – 'No, I'm a physician' – would invariably be met with the clouding over of their face. One would then have to explain that not all hospital specialists spend their days in the operating theatre carrying out surgical procedures...

For much of my time as a consultant physician for the NHS, most of my physician colleagues in hospital medicine and I were expected to take part in the 'acute' – emergency – general medicine on-call rota, whatever our particular specialty was. 'General medicine' in this case referred to all patients who were not surgical. In other words, we were responsible for admitting patients with heart attacks, heart failure, kidney failure, pneumonias, collapsed lungs, asthma, chronic bronchitis, strokes, cancers, overdoses, inflammatory bowel conditions, diarrhoea and vomiting, infections and septicaemia... the list went on. One of the challenges and attractions of being responsible for emergency medical admissions was that you never knew what you would come across around the corner. While many of the medical cases admitted were for predictable problems – such as the significant number of patients with chronic chest disease, who arrived with severe breathing difficulties due to chest infections and pneumonia, especially during the winter months – there were always surprises.

One Friday evening I was on the Medical Admissions Unit with the senior house officer and house physician doing a round of all the medical admissions who had arrived that day, when our registrar came hurrying up to me. 'There's a very sick patient I think you should see first, Jeremy,' he said. We went straight to the bay at the end of the ward, where there was indeed a very sick woman in her thirties. She was semi-conscious, flushed with a high fever and breathing very fast. She was also showing signs of cerebral irritation; constantly plucking at the bed sheets with her hands in an agitated and involuntary fashion. I lifted up her head gently with my hand to find that her neck was rigid and came up with it. She was clearly presenting with septicaemia (blood poisoning) and meningitis (inflammation of the tissue surrounding the brain and spinal cord), most likely,

I thought, as a result of infection with the pneumococcus pneumonia bug. Later tests proved this clinical diagnosis to be correct. Her husband Luke was standing at her bedside, understandably agitated, with their three-year-old daughter in his arms. 'Jayne caught this bug from Lucy here about three days ago,' he said to me. 'It only seemed like a simple cold. She was OK until this morning, when she became suddenly very ill. Our daughter seems to be getting better, but I think I'm going down with it myself,' he coughed, as if to prove the point.

Within seconds we had taken blood cultures from the patient, inserted a cannula into a vein in her arm, commenced intravenous fluids and started treatment with intravenous antibiotics. We then took the brakes off her bed and wheeled her ourselves straight to the Intensive Therapy Unit, one of the Medical Admissions Unit staff nurses telephoning the staff there to let them know that we were on our way. On the ITU, Jayne was sedated and put on a ventilator, which took over her breathing for her. The plan was to continue the intravenous antibiotics with her sedated and ventilated for twenty-four to forty-eight hours at least, while monitoring and protecting her kidney function and vital signs, in the hope that we had caught the fulminating and life-threatening infection in time. However, I was not optimistic about her chances of survival.

I knew from the experience I had had with the condition during my time at Addenbrooke's Hospital in Cambridge and elsewhere that pneumococcal septicaemia and meningitis was every bit as fatal as the more classical meningococcal variety. The pneumococcus bacterium, which is often the cause of 'straightforward' pneumonia, could cause sudden death if it breached the barriers into the brain and circulation, causing meningitis and the circulation to collapse as fluid suddenly drained out of the system. Luckily, this remains a rare complication with this common bug. But when it does occur the result is often very rapidly lethal.

When I had finished seeing the other twenty or so medical patients who had been admitted so far that day, I went back to the ITU on my way home to check on Jayne. Her condition had stabilised; her heart was beating fast due to the infection but maintaining a reasonable blood pressure with the help of 'pressor' drugs, and her kidneys were still producing adequate amounts of urine into the catheter which was monitoring its flow. I left the hospital that night, however, knowing that her chances of survival were no better than fifty-fifty at best. The next twenty-four to forty-eight hours would be critical. She did at least have in her favour the fact that, before being struck down by this terrible infection, she had been a young, fit, healthy woman.

I was not called during the night, but when I came back into the hospital at about eight the next morning I made straight for the ITU. I was let in by my consultant anaesthetist colleague, who was in charge of the ITU for the weekend. In response to my anxious enquiry, he was able to tell me that Jayne's condition had at least remained stable during the night. As we neared her bed, however, I was shocked to see her husband Luke in the ITU bed next to her. He had been admitted via Casualty by my medical team on take after becoming much more unwell. The little girl remained fine and was being cared for by friends. Although Luke's condition had been concerning enough for him also to be admitted to the ITU for monitoring, he had not needed to be placed on a ventilator. However, he was also requiring intravenous fluids and antibiotics. Luckily he made a rapid recovery from there, and was well enough to be discharged home to convalesce after only a few days in hospital. His wife Jayne remained critically ill for many weeks, requiring a stay on the ITU of about three months in total. I am pleased to report, however, that she survived the illness without long-term damage to her health. I could not have been more delighted to meet up with her in my outpatient clinic some weeks after her discharge from hospital. She arrived with Luke and their daughter Lucy and was back to normal health. It was a pleasure to be able to discharge her from my hospital follow-up clinic.

So perhaps you are starting to get the idea that there is more to hospital medicine than just 'cutting things out' and 'sticking things in'?

2

Listening to Learn –
As a Medical Student

As a medical student you soon become aware of the fact that you learn much of what you need to know by listening, seeing and experiencing. Listening to and watching how doctors, nurses and others operate over time is an essential part of getting to grips with the art and science of medicine yourself. But somehow the *listening* part of the learning process as a trainee doctor has acquired a bad name in some circles. The 'passive' process of *listening* has been supplanted by the need for students in general to be 'educated', as if the delivery of knowledge is a one-way process. The traditional image of a student learning at the feet of his/her professor has also become unfairly stigmatised in this context as being outdated, although I can remember learning a great deal myself in this way.

Once they graduate to the hospital wards, during their final three years of clinical training, medical students are taught by doctors who are at the same time delivering their service to their patients. This means that, inevitably, these clinical medical students, who are being taught by hard-pressed senior doctors, may sometimes feel they are kept hanging around on a ward or in a clinic waiting for the teaching sessions to occur. But there is always so much to be learnt if they care to look around and listen in every corner of the ward or clinic where real things are happening. The ones who accept this with understanding and without complaint always make the best use of their time in the process.

Later on, having the chance to 'try it for yourself' is also an equally important part of the learning process: if doctors are to be given the responsibility for our lives – which they are – they should also be trusted in training to learn by practising, in both senses of the word. If this occasionally results in trainee doctors having to learn from making – hopefully not serious – mistakes, this is also an important part of the educational process: we need to have the honesty to acknowledge this. Too much about medical education is dictated these days by educationalists who have no experience themselves of this basic fact and no understanding about the importance of 'service delivery' in the process of 'training'. The delivery of service as a way of learning has acquired a dirty reputation with those in medical-training circles partly, perhaps, because of the antisocial long hours that medical students and junior doctors used to be expected to work, which were seen as exploitative. But little attention has really been paid in practice to how long training should take and how much of it should be focussed on 'doing' as well as 'listening' and 'watching'.

An example of this is that medical deaneries (who are responsible for policing the delivery of education to new doctors) often stipulate that junior doctors should not be asked to perform routine procedures, such as bladder catheterisation – the implication being that the requirement to perform a large number of this relatively simple but important procedure is exploiting doctors in training for a menial service reason which has no educational benefit. But they often do so without specifying how many catheterisations *would* be a good idea for doctors who are still training to undertake to become proficient at the procedure and – equally important – how few are therefore *not enough* to learn the procedure competently.

All aspects of the many varied sub-disciplines of medicine (including surgery) are fascinating if – like any other subject – they are taught well. But becoming interested in and even inspired by the theory of a subject is not the same thing as taking that discipline on as a job in real life. Dr Tony Brandfoot is an example which comes to my mind. He was a histologist by trade, a consultant histopathologist, who spent his life receiving little pieces – biopsies – of a patient's natural body, or a part of it affected by disease, such as a piece of a cancerous growth. He would mount these tiny slivers of tissue on to a glass slide, stain them with coloured stains, and peer at them under a microscope to classify them according to their cellular and chemical constituents. The service he provided was essential to physicians and surgeons alike in confirming the nature and type of the tissue. Not only was the outcome of his deliberations important to his doctor colleagues, but, of course, it goes without saying that his verdicts were also vital to the patient from which the tissue had been taken. His assessment would determine whether the tissue was innocent – 'benign' – or cancerous – 'malignant' – and, if the latter, what the type and stage of the cancer might be. In essence, his histological diagnosis directed the need for treatment and what the treatment should be. In simple terms, he was pronouncing on the life or death of the man or woman under his microscope.

Dr Brandfoot was one of the most enthusiastic teachers I can ever remember listening to. He was somewhere in his middle age, but dressed as he was in his corduroy jacket, grey flannel trousers and John Lennon circular wire glasses, his appearance was akin to that of Harry Potter. He would dance about the stage, pointing with his wooden wand at every little detail of a projected slide of one of his H & E (haemosiderin and eosin) stained pieces of tissue, magnified for all in the auditorium to see. The absolute enthusiasm he had for his subject could not but be infectious for his audience and was the reason why he was such an excellent teacher. It was difficult not to become interested in his passionate descriptions of the tissues on the screen.

But, when the dust had settled later in life, and you were considering what you wanted to 'do' as a doctor, it became necessary to ask yourself, would you really like to spend much of your professional days performing autopsies on dead patients (who had lost the ability to listen to you and talk back to you!) in the mortuary in the basement of the hospital? And the rest of the time in a darkened room in a laboratory, peering down a microscope at pieces of tissue that had been obtained from that cadaver or that some other doctor had obtained from his still living patient? Of course, notwithstanding these drawbacks, a career in histopathology is still attractive to some – perhaps those who are not so keen to be burdened by listening to and talking with patients? – but I frequently gave this as an example when discussing with medical students and young doctors what career paths they might take. I never pressurised any of them to take a particular path and, indeed, I never deliberately put anyone off a particular career. I always stressed, however, that there was often a wide gap between enjoying a subject in theory and putting it into practice for the rest of your life. The advice was always, 'Try it for yourself a bit first, before committing to it for good.'

3

Shifting Dullness

PROFESSOR HAROLD ELLIS WAS PROFESSOR OF SUR-
gery at Westminster Hospital Medical School, the University
of London. Like most professors, he was a proud man.
In his case, he had a lot to be proud of, being a national
and international authority on the practice of surgery and
having written, among others, the best-selling books *Clinical
Anatomy* and *Lecture Notes on Surgery*, the latter with the
equally eminent Roy Yorke Calne (later to become Sir Roy
Calne). But the thing that Harold Ellis took the greatest
pride in, he told us, was the fact that he had made his way
to his eminent position having been born and brought
up in a poor Jewish family in the East End of London.
He had 'pulled himself up by his shoestrings'. Indeed, he
would not hesitate to tell us, his students, that he had a
brother who was at the time still a barrow boy on the
Mile End Road.

Harold Ellis's foremost reputation was as an inspirational
teacher. His humorous and instructive lectures left a mark on
almost all of the medical students who were lucky enough to

come under his influence. For those of us who had not yet witnessed his skill as a surgical technician, it was clear that he was a great teacher. Ellis sowed the seeds of interest in his subject in all who listened to him, and he was responsible for persuading many of his audience to pursue a lifelong career in surgery. Many of those who studied and worked under his tutelage went on to become eminent surgeons in their own right.

One of the highlights of the introductory course for new clinical medical students was the lecture on surgery to be given by Professor Ellis himself. On the allotted morning, the professor walked in to the packed lecture theatre exactly on time wearing his starched white coat, buttoned up from his knees to his Adam's apple, and stood on the edge of the stage. 'My name's Ellis. I'm one of the surgeons here,' the professor started in a surprisingly modest but nevertheless authoritative manner. 'You, girl,' he then demanded, immediately pointing to a female medical student in the front row, 'what is the definition of shifting dullness?' (Shifting dullness is the physical sign elicited by percussing the abdomen of a patient whose belly is swollen by an accumulation of fluid. This may occur as a result of inflammation from disseminated cancer cells or caused by the loss of protein in the blood from the failing liver in severe liver disease, among other pathologies.)

'Well, sir,' came the young lady's frightened reply, 'you percuss the abdomen into the flank and then roll the patient on to his side...'

'You, boy,' Ellis interrupted, pointing at a young man next to the girl, having ignored the first attempted reply to his question.

'Well, sir...' the student said, waving his hands in the air and percussing the back of his left middle finger with the middle finger of his right hand. He was clearly unsure what to add further to the answer the girl next to him had given and was also summarily cut off without a word by the professor.

'You, girl!' Ellis continued to interrogate those students enthusiastic and unlucky enough to have sat in the front row of the lecture theatre, pointing at the next female medical student in the row. 'What's the definition of shifting dullness?' Ellis roared, giving the last poor young lady no time to even open her mouth. 'You 'orrible lot!' cried Ellis from the stage, 'I'm going to discard you all like a used condom' – and with that he thrust his right arm forward in a Hitler salute and then, with a grimace, released the thumb and forefinger of his right hand in mid-air while mouthing the appropriate onomatopoeic 'splat' as he did so. 'Let me tell you all – and don't you *ever* forget it!! The definition of shifting dullness is a *physician's ward round*. Good morning, ladies and gentlemen.' Thereupon, Ellis turned on his heel and walked out of the lecture theatre.

The whole class of first-year clinical medical students collapsed in floods of relief and hilarity. In that very short encounter, they had not yet learned anything about the mysteries of surgery. But they had started to understand what the rumours about the great surgeon were based on and were hungry to learn more from his lectures to come. In this day and age, the professor would most likely never have got away with it: he would probably have been reported for 'inappropriate behaviour' or even 'bullying of female medical students'. I suspect you can guess which era I consider the poorer? Although, I do have to say that, once I became qualified as a doctor and a junior house physician in the same hospital, it did become just a little wearying to walk down the hospital corridor behind my consultant physician boss and the rest of his 'firm' and find ourselves on the receiving end of the professor of surgery and his team as they passed us in the opposite direction – 'Watch out, men! There goes the Shifting Dullness!' – Professor Ellis's by then rather stale joke ringing in our ears.

4

Cutting Things Out

AS IT TURNED OUT, MY FIRST ATTACHMENT TO A SUR-
gical firm at Westminster Hospital Medical School was
with the team led by Mr Kingsley Robinson and Mr Charles
Westbury (known to everyone as 'Charlie'). Business here
was conducted at a different pace from that which I later
came to experience with Professor Harold Ellis. Kingsley
Robinson was a general surgeon, a quiet and thoughtful
man who would frequently interrupt his own ward round
by staring into space at the end of the bed as he listened
carefully to a patient's story and thought about the problem of the patient in front of him and what his strategy for
dealing with it should be. He was, in fact, an example of a
surgeon as a 'listening doctor'.

Mr Charlie Westbury was a highly intelligent and inno-
vative surgeon. Specialising as he did in cancers of the head
and neck, he undertook the dramatic operation of a hemi-
facectomy – removing half of the face of a patient in an
attempt to remove every possible evidence of cancer cells.
He was responsible for pioneering the technique of 'facial

flaps' – the use of flaps of muscle from other parts of the upper body still attached to their blood supply to act as a replacement for the drastic amount of tissue that had been removed with the cancer from the patient's head and face. Scattered around his ward one would see patients with one arm lifted up next to their face in a sling to support the connection of blood vessels coming from it. This blood supply was providing life for the transplanted tissue, in order for it to implant itself permanently on the side of the person's face that had otherwise been largely removed.

To look at Mr Westbury at first glance, one could not have guessed at his intellectual approach to the pioneering surgery he undertook. He was a small, short-sighted man with something of a stoop, who would stand at the end of the bed with his hands deep in his white coat pockets, blinking through his thick spectacles at his patient. The surgical registrar on the team at the time was a Mr Blake. Not unsurprisingly, the firm of Messrs Robinson and Westbury became widely known as 'Thinker, Blinker & Blake'.

At qualification, I was lucky enough to have been the only student in my year at Westminster Medical School to be awarded an Honours Viva in Surgery in the final examination. I should stress, however, that this did not mean that one was inevitably awarded Honours in Surgery, as turned out to be the result in my case. Students were chosen on the basis of their written paper in surgery for participation in the Honours Viva, which proved to be an additional oral examination that was held at the University of London

Senate House and consisted of a thorough grilling of perhaps thirty minutes or so by a couple of eminent surgeons from one of the other eleven London medical schools. I felt I was doing all right, but was aware that I had drawn a blank when asked if I could think of any association between pulmonary tuberculosis of the lung and peptic ulceration of the stomach. I could not think of one, and was cross with myself as I left the exam, realising that I had bombed on what was essentially a medical (as opposed to a surgical) topic.

Nevertheless, my minor success in the surgery exam of the final MB BS had clearly reached the ears of Professor Ellis. A few days later, while walking along Page Street at the back of Westminster Hospital one evening, the professor came up behind me and gripped me by the elbow. 'Ah, Bending,' Ellis enthused. 'Pleased I caught you. I'd like to invite you to apply to become my next house surgeon.' (All rather an exhibition of patronage, I remember feeling at the time, although undoubtedly well-meaning. But a step up, I suppose, from a century or more before when surgical house officers – or 'dressers' as they were called – actually had to pay an eminent surgeon for the privilege of working and learning the trade at his side!) I was taken aback, and it took me a few seconds to find my tongue in reply.

'That's very kind of you, sir,' I finally found the breath to reply. 'But the fact is,' I went on, as tactfully as I was able, 'I am keen to become a physician and have already applied for one of the house physician jobs here at Westminster.' 'Humph!' was all Ellis said as he turned away and walked off towards the hospital. I suppose he had never had a student turn down the offer of becoming his house surgeon before. As far as I can remember, he never spoke to me again.

When I told my story in the medical school bar later that evening, I was not surprisingly teased ragged by the other students there. In addition to the fact that those present were quite sure I did not deserve to have been offered this post, the general consensus was that I had turned the offer down because I was shy of the gruelling hours that this particular house job involved – many more than the amount required by any other house job at the time, and the rest demanded excessive hours by today's standards. As house surgeon to the professor of surgery, you were expected to be on call one in one; in other words working full time without a break – living in and on call day and night, seven days a week for the full six-month duration of the post. Ellis worked himself and all those on his firm equally hard. One famous example of this fact was that his registrar at the time, a man called Brian Heather, was said to have been allowed four hours off on a Saturday afternoon in June to go and get married. I never found out whether this apocryphal story was really true, but it certainly was consistent with the general work ethic that Ellis expected of himself and all those working with him. All I could do was swear to my mates in the bar that evening that this had nothing to do with why I had declined the professor's offer.

When I tell the doctors in training today about the hours that we as junior doctors were expected to work in the seventies, I am quite sure they think I'm telling porkies! I have also heard them saying that things cannot have been as busy then as they are now, which is not the case. For my part, I was ultimately pleased that I had listened to my heart as well as to my head.

5

Learning to Listen

My first house job after qualification as a doctor was working as a house physician at Westminster Hospital in London, where I had trained as a medical student. In those days, during the first year after qualifying, all new doctors were required to undertake a pre-registration year, which entailed working for six months in a hospital medical specialty and six months in a surgical specialty, before obtaining their full registration with the General Medical Council. We were what they call 'interns' in North America.

Working as a house physician and a house surgeon entailed being responsible for the day-to-day management of the inpatients under the care of the particular consultant or consultants whose team you were attached to. I used to refer to this as being 'Officer of the House', a term I still used with my own newly qualified house officers (known these days as Foundation Year 1 trainees – which doesn't have quite the same buzz, does it?) after I had become a consultant physician myself. I understood what a big step it was to change from being a 'listening medical student' to a 'listening doctor', but encouraged them to realise that they were now expected to start taking responsibility for their patients and their actions right from the beginning, with the understanding that they should feel able to ask for help or advice as often as they felt the need.

My first boss was a man called Dr Clarence Gavey, the senior physician at Westminster Hospital. He was an almost Dickensian character; a very portly man with a red face and beaked nose who would breathe heavily, his halitosis hitting you in the face, as he marched down the hospital corridors. He was a stickler for punctuality and would expect the whole of his team – the senior registrar, the registrar, the senior house officer and myself, the house physician – to be present in his office and on time for each of his meetings with us at the beginning and end of every day. These meetings would be held at 8.30 a.m. and 6.30 p.m. sharp, and I was expected to have a clipboard with an up-to-date list of all the patients in hospital under Dr Gavey's care, both those on Erskine (our base ward) and any patients who were 'outliers' on other wards. I would read down the list one by one and either myself or one of the registrars would update Gavey on the patient's progress or otherwise. I never knew how much he was listening to us, but every so often he would pull out a patient's X-ray from its brown envelope, put it on the X-ray screen and stand staring at it. 'Look here, doctor,' Gavey would say to no one in particular, 'There's *mischief* in the oesophagus!' and he would indicate what looked like a cancerous obstruction to be seen at the bottom end of the patient's gullet on the barium swallow X-ray. There wasn't too much humour to be had on this side of the firm. Dr Gavey was obsessional about making a careful carbon copy of every ECG heart tracing taken on every patient under his care. It was rumoured that he kept all of these tracings in piles of boxes in the attic of his house. Somehow I wasn't surprised to hear some years later that Dr Gavey himself had died from congestive cardiac failure. Doctors, it is said, always die of their own diseases.

My other boss as a house physician was Dr Peter Emerson. He was a complete contrast to Dr Gavey – sophisticated and urbane, usually nattily dressed in an expensive double-breasted suit with hair carefully combed back to one side and a crooked smile on his face; no doubt a ladies' man. Dr Emerson was a well-respected chest physician who worked part of the week at the Brompton Chest Hospital in London as well as consulting at Westminster Hospital. I used to listen to him carefully as he sat on a patient's bed and gently broke the news that the reason for the patient's breathlessness was that he had developed a cancer in his lung. Dr Emerson believed strongly, as did I, that it was the right of every patient to be fully informed about the details of his or her illness. This was not the norm in those days, when people were quite often left in the dark about what might be going on with their health. Indeed, the word cancer was usually not mentioned openly in front of a patient. Ros, the ward sister, was a lovely, devout Irish Catholic girl who had quite the opposite point of view, believing that it was not kind to tell her patients the truth. While I disagreed with Sister Ros on this point, I used to be fascinated by the fact that, in the end, those patients under 'Emmo''s care somehow seemed to receive as much information as they wanted to know and no more.

One of Dr Emerson's favourite tricks on his ward round – particularly with the arrival of a new house physician, such as myself – was to pick up the patient's plastic sputum pot from the bedside table, remove its top and stare at the contents before showing it to the various doctors and nurses around the bed. Most of us turned our heads away in respectful disgust after a cursory glance, but occasionally a doctor on the team would peer in to look at its contents with undisguised excitement. As the doctor's eyes lit up, you could almost hear him thinking, 'Purulent sputum. But look: also some *fresh blood* in it!' Dr Emerson would then explain to us that it was his way of finding out which of the doctors in training working on his firm were destined to follow in his footsteps as consultant chest physicians! I used to tell this story to young doctors who came to me for career advice when as a consultant I became the postgraduate clinical tutor at Eastbourne District General Hospital, a post I held for more than ten years – the message being that I can give you ideas and advice about how to go about it, but in the final analysis you do have to follow your heart as well as your head. It is no good finding yourself in a specialty or discipline, which you will be involved with for the rest of your professional life, if it doesn't really thrill you.

Like Dr Emerson, Dr Gavey also had consulting duties at another hospital, being a consulting physician at Moorefield's Eye Hospital in London. He also had a thriving private practice, consulting in his rooms in Harley Street. I soon learnt that he frequently admitted private patients under his care to what was the sixth floor at Westminster Hospital – the Private Patients Wing. It was not unusual for me to receive a bleep from the sister on the sixth floor at 7 p.m. on a Friday, just as I was due to get away for my first weekend off duty for three weeks, to tell me that there were 'three patients of Dr Gavey who have just arrived' and would I please come up. Each of these patients needed clerking and blood taking and so forth, which meant that I was not likely to get off for my weekend much before midnight. I would not have minded, but the boss never said thank you, let alone thought that some remuneration, or at least a bottle of something, might be in order.

This early experience confirmed my view that it is not appropriate to have a private wing in an NHS hospital. The effect on all the staff – nurses, porters, domestic cleaners and so on – is potentially divisive when the consultant is pocketing all the proceeds! I vowed then never to expect my junior colleagues to have to look after any private patient I might have when I became a consultant, something that I later always carried out in practice. If there was an occasional patient who asked to go to the private ward, I would look after them myself completely and not expect my junior colleagues to visit them daily or come with me to see them as part of my ward round.

6

Bring Back the Four-Letter Word

ON THE FIRST FIRM AT WESTMINSTER HOSPITAL FOR which I worked as a house physician – Dr Gavey's firm – the senior registrar was Dr John Thurston, an ebullient character who made a point of correcting my language and that of every other member of the team. My ward round presentation starting with, 'This pleasant fifty-six-year-old lady...' would be met with the riposte, 'How do you know she's pleasant, Bending, you're not married to her!' He had a point, although I am not sure how many wives he's had in the intervening years! Always interested in words, his teaching ensured that ever after I took great care about how they were used, and how they were used in medicine in particular; something that I tried to pass on to those I was to train later myself. This early lesson I received about the importance of being careful with my use of words and labels also taught me to be careful about not making value judgements about patients who came under my care, especially if they were seriously ill.

One Friday morning I was called to the Medical Admissions Ward to clerk a man in his forties in kidney failure who had been admitted as an emergency. He was seriously ill, but also unkempt and dirty, unshaven with matted hair and had offensive breath caused by his uraemic foetor – the strong smell of urea which occurs on the breath of patients in kidney failure. I treated him with respect, as I did with all my patients, but remember asking myself at the back of my mind, 'How on earth could he have allowed himself to get into this state without asking for help much earlier?'

On Monday morning, after a weekend off duty, I went to see the patient again on the Renal Unit. I could not believe my eyes. He was sitting on a chair next to his bed, washed and closely shaven with clean, carefully combed hair. He was also fully dressed in a blue shirt and tie and an expensive pin-striped suit. The sessions he had had on the kidney dialysis machine over the weekend had transformed him. 'Wow, Robin,' I said, blinking at him enthusiastically, 'don't *you* look better!'

'Thanks,' he replied appreciatively. I inspected the drug chart at the end of the bed, noting the long list of supportive drugs he was now receiving.

'By the way,' I said to him before I left to return to the Medical Admissions Unit, 'I forgot to ask you, what do you do for a living?'

'I'm a barrister at law,' Robin replied, giving me a huge grin. 'So much for the tramp I took him for on Friday!' I thought to myself, as I wished him well and left the ward.

I had always known in theory that it was wrong to label people, especially on first meeting, and this patient taught me the importance of observing the rule in practice. A lesson I never forgot. So, from early on in my career I learnt to use words precisely and appropriately – medicine is a science as well as an art – and at the same time to do my very best to get to know my patients as people, not just as medical labels.

The abstract of a recent paper in the *British Medical Journal* brought me up with a start: 'Treatment with angiotensin receptor blockers (a group of blood pressure-lowering drugs) is not associated with a significantly increased risk of myocardial infarction (heart attacks) ... our findings may alleviate recent concerns over the safety of this class of *medications*.' Well that's all right then, I thought, particularly since I'm swallowing one myself. But what's wrong with using the word *'drug'* these days? The word which has been used in medicine for many decades seems to have gone out of favour, probably tainted by an association with illegal and so-called 'social' substances. The *Drug and Therapeutics Bulletin* has not changed its name (yet), but the Committee on Safety of Medicines is treading a politically correct fine line. If the registrar or senior house officer used the word *medication* when dictating a patient discharge report or clinic letter, my secretary had instructions to type the four-letter word *drug*. And I couldn't help squirming in grand rounds when junior and not-so-junior colleagues repeated the line about patients being 'on' drugs, rather than 'taking' them.

Since we're on the subject, the four-letter word 'died' is another example. I was met one morning by my house physician (sorry, Foundation Year 1 doctor) with the news that Mr Sanderson (who had been expected to die) had 'passed away' in the night. While that might (just) have been a helpful statement for the nurses to make to his wife, I am not sure it is appropriate talk between professionals. We all know that language is constantly evolving, a process influenced by cultural and national factors, among other things. I also blame the word processor. The worst howler I have come across recently involving the latter was in a letter from a senior hospital manager in reply to a complaint from a grieving widow. In the first paragraph he expressed his 'sincere condolences for your sad loss' and in the fifth paragraph wrote, 'Please convey my best wishes to your husband for a speedy recovery.' But I digress: the point is that electronic words do not necessarily make for clarity or precision in writing. In my experience, the word processor often encourages the use of lengthy words, where a four-letter one would have sufficed.

7

Listening to Pain

MY SIX-MONTH HOUSE SURGERY JOB WAS QUITE A CON-
trast to the house physician job at Westminster Hospital that
I had just left. I was working for three consultant surgeons:
Messrs Jenkins, Notley and Schweitzer at the Royal Surrey
County Hospital and St Luke's Hospital in Guildford, Surrey.
'Jenks' was a general surgeon who seemed game to try his
hand at anything and everything, sometimes in quite a cav-
alier fashion, it seemed to me. I met him in the surgeons'
changing room on my first morning. I was rather tentatively
deciding what pieces of the green pyjamas I had been given
I would need to put on when he jumped out from behind
the locker door where he had been changing himself. 'You
working with me?' was his immediate question. 'Thought
so. Can you tie knots?' was all he said in response to my reply
in the affirmative. Not exactly unfriendly, but certainly not
exhibiting the welcoming commitment to a new 'Foundation
Year 1' trainee that would be expected these days!

The first operation of the morning was an open chole-
cystectomy (gall bladder removal) on an obese lady who had

been suffering from gall stones. The procedure seemed to take hours, during which I was required to stand very still, pulling hard on the large metal clamp which was keeping the lady's folds of fat out of Jenks's way as he operated deep into her abdomen. Every so often he pointed to a suture which he had just knotted carefully around an artery, indicating that he required me to cut the unwanted ends off at a precise length. The fact that I was not very adept even at this basic manipulation soon labelled me in Mr Jenkin's eyes as a doctor who was not going to make a surgeon. It was a factor among many which persuaded me also that the surgical 'craft' was not for me. But I do not think that my lack of dexterity in the practical sense was responsible for the fact that a number of Jenks's operations did not seem to go well, ending up with the patient having to return to theatre because of post-operative bleeding or bowel leakage. Luckily, the surgical registrar was a highly enthusiastic and very practised surgeon from Hong Kong called Eddie Lim. Eddie would open you up, whip out your appendix or whatever and have you back in the ward and fine before you knew what had happened! He was also a good teacher and a supportive colleague.

Messrs Notley and Schweitzer were both urological surgeons. Richard Notley was a very experienced urologist who had previously worked as a reader in urology (a university position) at the London Hospital. He was a didactic teacher and I have a persisting memory of him calling me over to wonder at the difference between urine which was mixed with a good deal of frank blood ('claret', in Mr Notley's words) compared to that with a smaller amount of blood ('rosé'). His point was that it does not take very much blood in your urine for it to look really quite a bit red. His consultant colleague, Mr Frank Schweitzer, was a relative – nephew, I think – of the fabled Dr Albert Schweitzer of East Africa fame. He was a softly spoken man with a handshake which seemed to me to fit with his very Christian persona.

One of the things that my surgery house job did help me with was learning to listen to patients in pain and assess their problem correctly. The diagnostic conundrum of a patient presenting with an acute painful abdomen was a challenging one. The cause could be anything from appendicitis, a blocked or perforated bowel or kidney stones to a cyst on the ovary, to name just a few possibilities. It was a good lesson in how to listen very carefully to the precise details of a patient's complaint and to weigh them all up in a sympathetic but systematic way. It was also necessary for a good surgeon to be able to think laterally, to not forget that a lot of other pathologies – such as a heart attack, for instance – could present atypically from time to time with pain in the belly rather than in the chest.

The way a good doctor listens to their patient is no better demonstrated than in the way that doctor assesses pain in all its guises. And to arrive at the right diagnosis from the history alone is a very rewarding result. I will never forget the gratitude I received from plenty of the men who had been admitted with abdominal pain, agitation and sometimes confusion resulting from acute urinary retention (blockage of the flow of urine leading to obstruction of the bladder, usually the result of an enlarged prostate gland in men), often at about two in the morning. After I had diagnosed the cause of their symptoms and passed a catheter into their bladder to relieve the severe discomfort which had often literally caused them to be climbing up the walls in agitation, they were always eternally grateful. In the wrong place, at the wrong time, the patient may have been given an injection of a drug to sedate them, in the misapprehension that they were presenting with some form of acute anxiety condition. Which they were of course, in the physical sense!

There is no doubt that being on the receiving end is a most important way for any doctor to learn how it must be for his or her patients. In my case, I have experienced pain in my life on a number of occasions. The first of these was in my next job when I was working as a medical senior house officer (SHO) in Croydon. I had had a very busy day and night admitting acutely ill patients with all sorts of medical problems. Amongst these were four men whom I had admitted to the Coronary Care Unit (CCU) with heart attacks. Three of them were desperately ill and in heart failure and, when I finally went to bed myself at about 3 a.m., I was not optimistic about their chances of still being alive in the morning.

I woke at about 7 a.m. with very severe abdominal pain. This was something which I had never experienced in my life before then. I knew I had to get up to check on my ill patients, and struggled to reach the Coronary Care Unit to do so. As I entered the unit I looked around at the four men in the beds to see with relief that not only were they all alive, but they were all sitting up in bed eating breakfast. At that moment, standing there in the middle of the unit, I retched and vomited all over the CCU floor. The CCU sister ushered me out of the door as her colleague searched for a bucket and mop to clear up my vomit. After having been carried down to the A & E Department, the consensus was that I had probably developed acute appendicitis. I was adamant that I did not want to go through the indignity of having to undergo surgery in my own hospital. My fellow medical SHO Harry Casey, a short, swarthy young Irish man from County Cork whose eyebrows met in the middle, kindly agreed to drive me up to Westminster Hospital in his car. I endured the ride in his Morris Minor up Streatham High Street vomiting out of the passenger window as we went.

In the A & E Department at Westminster Hospital I was put on a couch in a cubicle waiting to be seen. The curtain was thrown open by John Poundsford, who was the on-call house surgeon of the day and had been a student in the year below me. He burst into fits of laughter – I don't blame him for that! – but also made it clear that he couldn't possibly admit somebody whom he knew well! So the task was left to his registrar, who did so in a professional manner. I was taken to theatre and my inflamed appendix removed without incident.

As I lay in my hospital bed recovering, I could not help but be reminded of an apocryphal story about the famous comic Eric Morecombe. He had been performing in a pantomime on the pier at Blackpool, when he developed severe chest pains, the beginning of his first heart attack, and was taken under a blue light to the Emergency Department at Blackpool Hospital. Apparently, as Eric struggled in through the door grasping his chest, the whole of the department recognised him and everybody fell about in stitches assuming that the comedy star was paying a charity visit to their hospital. Supposedly, it took quite a while for the penny to drop, and for his problem to be taken seriously.

Over the years I have experienced a number of episodes of renal colic – pain caused by the contraction of the kidney tubes against a kidney stone which is blocking them. This is said – by men – to be 'the worst pain known to man'. The implication being, I believe, that 'if you girls think childbirth is painful, I've had something even worse!' Let me correct those men with a history of renal colic: the pain, though excruciating, is nothing like that which as a mature consultant I also experienced one day after developing a completely obstructed and infected left kidney. I had just driven a Luton van full of furniture from Budapest to Eastbourne – an 1800 km drive on my own across Central and Western Europe in thirty-six hours, which included sleeping on the front bench seat of the vehicle in the bitter cold of an early morning in the French Alps. I was bringing the stuff back from an apartment we were selling after my youngest son had finished studying in Budapest. Having unloaded the van at home and returned the vehicle to the hire company, I awoke the next morning with pain even worse than any of the previous bouts of renal colic.

I was admitted to my own hospital's Emergency Department in Eastbourne and seen by one of my consultant surgeon colleagues on call. When he could not be sure what was going on, he passed me over to one of my most trusted surgical colleagues, who arranged for me to have a CT scan of my abdomen. This showed that my left kidney was obstructed and had expanded to about the size of a rugby ball. I was therefore passed on to one of my consultant urology colleagues. I felt as though I were a hot potato, being passed from hand to hand as quickly as possible before the music stopped! I lay in severe pain for some days, pain that was not touched by the morphine I was being pumped full of. I had been transferred to a room on the Private Patients Unit as an NHS patient, a gesture of recognition by the surgeons that I was a senior colleague presenting as a patient. For a number of days and nights I could find no relief from the excruciating pain. I would be awake all night trying out of honour to tolerate it until, one morning at about 3 a.m., I had no choice but to ring the bell for help. After some minutes a cheery nursing assistant arrived and turned the bell off. 'Don't worry, dear,' she said, 'I'll call the staff nurse to come in and see you.' But nobody came. In fact, during the whole ten days I was a patient on the unit, the sister in charge did not come in to say hello to me once. I tell this story not because I still feel sorry for myself – which I certainly did at the time! – but because it was a very sobering experience and an education for me, even at an advanced stage of my career, to learn what many of my own patients might be undergoing on a daily basis. It also served to reinforce my worst concerns about the deteriorating quality of nursing care in our hospitals.

8

Not Listening to the Patient

MICHAEL HAD BEEN A BIG BEAST OF A MAN. HE WAS A bricklayer by trade and had been proud of his normally tanned and sweat-glistening torso and bulging muscles, especially his biceps. He had developed acute myeloid leukaemia and was now in the specialist leukaemia unit receiving treatment. He had been given chemotherapy to ablate (destroy) his cancerous bone-marrow cells and was now waiting for a bone-marrow transplantation. He was bald as a coot, having lost all of his hair, from his entire body as well as his head, as a result of the chemotherapy. He had also lost a significant amount of his body weight. His limbs were like matchsticks, the previously bulging muscles having dissolved to sinew, his face sunken and his eyes had shrunk into their grey sockets. He was bruising very easily all over his body and he was bleeding from his gums. Because he had no functioning bone marrow remaining – the normal bone marrow having been destroyed along with the cancerous cells – he had lost the ability to make normal white blood cells, and his natural immunity from infection as a result. He was therefore being cared for in one of the 'reverse barrier' nursing rooms on the unit. This meant that none of his relatives or other visitors could enter the room, because of the risk of exposing him to any infection whatsoever, which could be fatal for him. All they could do was stand outside his small room and talk to him through a large Perspex window which covered its front wall. When we, the doctors and nurses, went in to see him we had to dress up in thick padded space suits, visor masks and gloves, not unlike the pictures shown recently of the outfits used by health care workers fighting the Ebola epidemic in West Africa.

'How are you feeling, Mike?' I asked him as I waddled into his room through the sealing double doors. Fully kitted out as I was, I felt like the Michelin Man from the car tyre advert.

'OK, I suppose, doc,' he replied. 'I think I've got another bout of fever coming.'

'That's what I thought,' I said, looking at the temperature chart in my hand. 'Has your wife been in to visit you yet today?' Mike had a lovely wife and two beautiful young kids. She came in to see him at least once every day, even though they lived a good distance away and she was carrying the family, the house and two schoolchildren all on her own at that moment. It never ceased to impress me how cheerful and positive she seemed able to be, at least in front of her husband. I suspected that things might have been different once she left to go home after each visit.

'I'm expecting her any minute, after she's picked the kids up from school. I wish they could be allowed to come in here and give me a cuddle,' he said, tears suddenly welling up in his eyes. 'I just miss being touched.'

'I know,' I said, putting my spaceman's arm around his shoulder. 'You'll just have to make do with a cuddle from me at the moment!' At this we both burst out laughing. I had been there long enough to understand that the one thing all of my patients really wanted in the reverse barrier unit was physical contact and the chance to be cuddled by their loved ones. Unfortunately, this was the one part of the healing process that was denied them there.

After finishing my house jobs – six months in medicine as a house physician at the Westminster Hospital where I had trained, followed by six months as a house surgeon down in Guildford – and a job as a senior house officer (SHO) in medicine in Croydon, I had been appointed to a locum post as an SHO on the Leukaemia Unit at the Royal Marsden Hospital in Surrey, while waiting to take up another substantive SHO job in intensive care medicine. The Marsden was a world-renowned unit – and still is – on the cutting edge of the fight to beat leukaemia, cancers that affect white blood cells. All of the patients on the unit were there because they had volunteered to receive the various cocktails of cancer chemotherapy that were being pioneered and tested in clinical trials. The purpose of these trials was to add to the ever-growing pool of information which was, bit by bit, leading towards a much-improved prognosis for the various fatal blood diseases, and to the cures for many of them that we now have today. The idea of ablating the bone marrow and replacing it with a healthy marrow transplant was revolutionary but in its infancy. Once he had received his transplant – most likely from his sister – I knew that it would be a long time before Michael could stop taking drugs aimed at preventing his own body rejecting the transplanted cells.

The ward rounds on the Leukaemia Unit took place every day and were conducted in the boardroom at the end of the unit. There were usually five or six senior doctors present, including one or two professors of leukaemia and a professor of haematology (the study of blood disorders), at least. They would gather round the huge boardroom table and paw over large sheets of logarithmic graph paper showing the results of the patients' daily blood tests, intensely interested in the direction that the blast-cell count was taking for each particular patient. The absence of blast cells suggested that the chemotherapy was keeping the leukaemia under control. A line going up, indicating that the blast-cell numbers were rising inexorably, was less good news.

I sat at the edge of the room listening to the discussions with my other SHO colleague, fascinated by the jargon but particularly interested in the results of those patients that I was looking after myself. I was waiting to hear what news, positive or negative, I would shortly be required to break to them. The patients all knew at what time the daily rounds were held, and they all fully understood by now the implications of the changes in the detailed haematological indices. On the basis of the results in front of them, the professors would be deciding whether a particular patient could now be regarded as clear, and therefore ready to come off treatment; could have relapsed, and therefore be offered yet another course of more toxic treatment, with its horrible side effects; or perhaps had come to the end of the line, which meant that the therapeutic treatment would be changed to palliative care, aimed at controlling the patient's symptoms as he or she died. My heart sank for Michael as I learnt that he had now been placed in the final group. It was clear that he was not going to live long enough to get his sister's marrow transplant. I was miserable at the thought that I was going to have to break this news to him, as well as to his wife and two small children.

As the ward round meeting wound up, the professors and other consultants dispersed to their clinics and laboratories. The details of the treatment plans agreed on were left to myself and my other SHO colleague to be passed on to our patients. I knew that it was not that the seniors did not care. It was that most of them were just too busy (apart from occasional exceptions) to spend time listening to each individual patient personally and 'breaking bad news', if that was to be the case. I understood their pressures completely. It was just that I was sure an important link was being missed in the successful treatment process. And this was the reason why I decided not to apply for a substantive post on the Leukaemia Unit once my locum three-month period had come to an end.

I know things are completely different now, nearly forty years later. The Royal Marsden Hospital remains renowned not only for its results but also for the care and compassion the doctors and cancer specialist nurses give, including to those who have reached the stage of end-of-life palliative care. I know, because patients have told me so on a regular basis.

9

Listening to the Music

MARTIN WAS A YOUNG MAN IN HIS EARLY TWENTIES. He was a professional guitarist who was just starting to make an important name for himself. Indeed, that week he had been performing his first solo concert at the Wigmore Hall in London, a prestigious venue and a challenge for any young musician making their mark. Unfortunately, the concert had not gone well. For some reason, which Martin could not explain, he had found himself fluffing his notes on quite a number of occasions, and particularly at a couple of critical points in important passages. He had never ever done this while performing before and could not understand why it had happened now. He had had a sore throat for about three days before the concert, but he would not normally have let this bother him. The review of the concert in *The Times* the next day was sympathetic because he was a young man giving his first concert at such a prestigious venue, but the newspaper's music critic was unable to give an honest report without mentioning these lapses.

Three days later Martin was rushed into the Accident &
Emergency Department of Charing Cross Hospital. He was
severely paralysed and hardly breathing. He was brought
straight up on the ambulance stretcher to the Intensive
Therapy Unit (ITU) where I was working on the thirteenth
floor of the hospital. I had only just started my senior house
officer job there that week. Apart from the Casualty SHO
who had come up in the lift with the patient, I was the only
doctor on duty in the unit. I did not have time to assess the
situation in detail, or indeed to hesitate. It was clear that the
young man was unconscious and about to have a respiratory
arrest (to stop breathing) and needed to be put on a ventilator immediately. Lifting Martin's chin up with one hand, I
held out the other to receive the silver metal laryngoscope
torch that the ITU staff nurse by my side was passing to
me. Using this to lift the tongue and soft palate, I was able
to gain a good view of the vocal cords and pass the plastic
endotracheal tube down into Martin's trachea (windpipe) at
the first attempt. I injected air down into the balloon around
the ET tube to secure it, as the nurse fitted a black rubber
bag to the end of the tube and started to squeeze. We both
relaxed as we saw Martin's chest start to rise and fall, his
heart rate picking up, and the grey-blue hue around his lips
and extremities start to become pink once more. This was
the first time I had been required to perform this particular
procedure unsupervised in a life-and-death situation.

After I had attached the breathing tube to the ventilator and let the machine take over the task of breathing

for him, the crisis had passed and I was able to reassess Martin's condition in more detail. His limbs were completely flaccid and I could elicit no tendon reflexes using the rubber tendon hammer on his elbows and knees. The signs were typical of a condition known as Guillain-Barré syndrome, a disease that can cause rapid paralysis of all the peripheral nerves in the body – including those nerves operating the chest and its breathing muscles. The condition can occur as a consequence of a simple infection such as food poisoning or a viral infection (post-infective polyneuropathy, to give it its other name). So it was the mild sore throat which had caused the problem and led to Martin fluffing his notes at the concert in the early stage of the disease, as he started to lose control of the muscles in his fingers on the strings of his guitar. When I subsequently heard the full story from Martin's parents, I thought to myself that I hope someone explains all this to the *Times*'s music correspondent in due course, to avoid any damage to Martin's musical reputation. We rolled Martin over on his side and I performed a lumbar puncture, obtaining a small amount of the fluid around his spinal cord, the analysis of which under the microscope subsequently confirmed my diagnosis.

Patients on ventilators are, or course, deeply sedated and unconscious. That is until their sedation is weaned off to assess when they might be able to breathe again on their own, unaided. Nevertheless, as doctors and nurses we do continue to speak to these unconscious and ventilated patients as if they can hear us. This is in the hope, I believe, that one day they might indeed hear what we are saying to them. But also, I feel, it helps all those of us caring for the unconscious person to treat him or her with respect and to maintain his or her dignity and, in the process, to maintain ours. Nurses working on intensive care units spend all their lives looking after patients whom they have never met before and who remain unconscious for most of their time on the unit. This carries with it the risk of the patients becoming dehumanised in the minds of the staff caring for them. I was always relieved when this did not seem to have occurred with patients under my care on the ITU, although I can also think of a number of instances when it did.

Music is often played to patients on the ITU. In Martin's case, I encouraged his mother to bring in tapes he would know and like, which she did enthusiastically. Some of these were recordings on the guitar which he had made himself. I would sit at his bedside in rapt appreciation of the young man's talents as I listened to his playing of Villalobos's and Albinoni's beautiful music for guitar. Indeed, I would frequently turn the volume up high, inviting the nurses and other colleagues in the unit to share with me in the pleasure of what I was listening to.

Music has always played an important part in our lives. It is a good way for doctors to cope with their stress. I had myself often enjoyed playing my clarinet, at one point in the past becoming proficient enough to play in a jazz band called The Wall Street Crash. Together with the other members of the group, not all medics, I would have a great time as well as earning a bit of pocket money. I have kicked myself for not being disciplined enough to keep this up. But, along with many other dreams, playing my clarinet is something I sincerely mean to return to when I can find the time.

Over the past couple of decades, I supervised a special study module (SSM) entitled 'Medicine & Music' for medical students from King's College Hospital in London and Brighton & Sussex Medical Schools who were in their final year of training and attached to our hospital. It was one of a myriad of topics, not all of them strictly medical by any means, which the students could pick for their final extra-curricular study prior to qualifying. Probably about once a year, on average, I would receive an email from a young male or female student with an interest in music who was enthusiastic to take up this challenge. I would meet up with them to find out what the reason for their interest in music was – often many of them had reached a very high level of proficiency in one or more instruments, including the voice – and then leave them to their own devices. Occasionally, they would email me back with questions or asking for advice, but usually I was as curious to hear what aspect the student had chosen to present as the rest of the audience sitting in the Lecture Theatre two months later on the day of the presentations.

The results were wide-ranging. Some had chosen to investigate the role of music in therapy, by visiting a unit for mentally disabled children and seeing how it was used in this setting, for example. Others had explored the biographies of famous musicians and conductors who had started out as doctors – and there are many of them – and others had looked at the way in which ordinary doctors use music for work and simple relaxation. The music available to patients on the console above their beds (which also provided a very mini TV screen) received a universal 'thumbs down'. This was largely because it was very expensive – the patients or their relatives had to keep feeding a meter with money to keep the thing running – and the medical students held the not unreasonable view that this was a service that perhaps the hospital should provide for free.

Quite a number of students over the years chose the topic of 'music in the medical workplace'. One fellow visited an operating session of every operating theatre and every surgeon in our hospital and asked all members of the surgical team, including not only the surgeons themselves, but anaesthetists, nursing staff and operating assistants, to fill out a questionnaire exploring what music they preferred (if any) to be played whilst surgery was going on and who got to choose. The answer to the latter question was usually 'the consultant surgeon himself', whatever the preferences of the rest of his team might be! I smiled to myself as I played music to my unconscious patient Martin on the ITU, relaxed in the knowledge that I had chosen music which I knew he would enjoy, although the nurses and I did too. Not least because he had played and recorded much of what we were listening to himself before he was struck down by this terrible illness.

Unfortunately, Martin's illness was not straightforward. He remained unconscious and on the ventilator for something like three months. During this time, we had to battle with more than one episode of hospital-acquired pneumonia and infections of his urinary tract, not to mention fungal infections occurring in his mouth and gullet and other parts of his body. He also developed life-threatening bouts of acute tachy-brady syndrome – his heart rate racing away wildly before slowing down alarmingly, with huge fluctuations of very high and very low blood pressure – as a result of the disease affecting the nerves of autonomic function, which regulate heart rate and breathing among other vital functions.

When Martin finally started to breathe again on his own, to the point where he had been weaned off the ventilator and had had a tracheostomy tube inserted into his windpipe in his neck, through which he breathed, Sister Rose came to speak to me: 'Do you know, Jeremy, I think Martin is blind.' It turned out that this was indeed the case. The disease had clogged his cerebrospinal fluid with large amounts of protein, which had led to very high pressure pressing on his brain and on the main optic nerves at the back of his eyes, leaving him without sight. I was mortified that I had not considered this possibility. But, in reality, there was no way of assessing this while he was sedated and still on the ventilator. I used to try and console myself on Martin's behalf that the loss of his sight in itself was something that would not necessarily preclude him from playing his guitar again. I was sure there must be some blind classical guitarists in the world out there?

I went to visit Martin a number of times after he had been transferred from the ITU to the neurology ward. But in due course he was transferred out of our hospital to a long-stay neuro-rehabilitation unit somewhere in Wiltshire. I heard nothing more about whether he had survived and what his eventual long-term recovery might have been, if so. For many years I found myself scouring the newspaper for the Wigmore Hall concert programmes, but never saw his name appear on them again.

10

Listening to the Drums

IN MY FINAL YEAR AS A CLINICAL MEDICAL STUDENT AT Westminster Hospital Medical School, I went off to Africa for my medical elective period. I had accepted an attachment for three months at Korle Bu Hospital Medical School in Accra, the capital of Ghana on the West Coast of Africa. Two years previously, during the long summer vacation between finishing my BSc degree and going on to Westminster Hospital Medical School to commence my clinical training, I had spent a few months working for the United Nations Students' Organisation in Uganda. I can still remember my mother, when confronted by the news that I was now planning an elective in West Africa, responding with the retort, 'Why do you want to go there? You've already been to Africa!' I did not have the energy to tell her that Kampala and Accra are more than 2,000 miles apart, and goodness knows how many days driving if you were to even attempt to travel between the two capitals by road.

Arriving in Ghana, I immediately felt completely at home. I cannot think of any other country I have visited where the people are so outgoing and friendly. Walking along the sea road past the municipal prison on my first Saturday in Accra, I came across a man of about fifty who was walking in the opposite direction. On seeing me, he hurriedly crossed to my side of the road to shake my hand vigorously in welcome. This was a genuine and spontaneous act, with no ulterior motive apart from simple friendship. He was not out to sell anything to me or get anything out of me. Having made his introduction, he insisted on inviting me to a small bar just up the road, where he bought us both a beer and we spent a pleasant time exchanging our views on life. I soon got used to the idea that Ghanaians are like this – a naturally very friendly and outgoing people. They also tend to be happy most of the time, whatever their individual lot in life.

The medical school and its students were the same. I became particularly friendly with Graham Knight, an intelligent and stimulating young Ghanaian man who was a student leader and one of the movers and shakers in his year. He was about six foot three, with joints so supple he seemed like a large puppet at times. He had a rather loose mop of curly black hair and pebble glasses. He could have been a Harlem Globetrotter. He was clearly a serious student but also the life and soul of the student fraternity. We used to spend a good deal of time sitting on the stools in the medical school bar drinking beer together, listening to each other's stories, talking about putting the world to rights and all sorts of issues and learning a lot from each other in the process. But this was not time that, in my opinion, was in any way wasted. The fact that one evening I put my right hand down hard on a beer glass which shattered under it was quite coincidental! I had to be taken to the Casualty Department of Korle Bu Hospital, where I was treated with great respect while the lacerations were sutured. The faint scars remain on my fingers to this day. Whenever I choose to look down and notice them, they warmly remind me of the welcome I received there.

While on attachment in Ghana, I went alone on a bit of a walkabout for a few days up north from Accra: first to Kumasi, the capital of the Ashanti Region, and finally reaching the remote northern town of Tamale. I travelled mainly by multi-coloured mammy wagons in the African tradition, heaving with brightly dressed Ghanaian trades-women, their kids, vegetables, hens and all. The incessant din of children crying, women shouting and laughing, hens and geese squawking and the bodily thump of the highly painted and decorated minibus as it bore down into a deep pot hole and out the other side still lives with me today. We would constantly be aware of the beat of drums, either for real in the villages in which we paused briefly or in the Highlife music that would blare out from the mammy wagon's loud speakers as it continued on its way.

Tamale was a town much like any other African com-munity I've encountered. There was one principal high street which, being the focus of the town's activities, was inevitably the place where the mammy wagons set down and picked up, as well as the location for the bustling market.

Along the length of the high street was a concrete row of shops of all descriptions, selling everything and anything you could wish to buy. The goods on sale were sometimes new, but there was also a huge range of second-hand items. The former included linens, cloths and clothes of all types and sizes as well as tinned foods, grain and seeds. The latter included electrical items, motor parts for trucks and cars, plumbing items and utensils and hardware of all sorts. Many of the shops were run by immigrants; people of Asian and Lebanese origin being prominent amongst them. The busiest trade, however, took place on the side of the road, where the street market bustled from dawn to dusk, seven days a week. This was the territory of the Ghanaian women. They were the 'Mammies' whom I had been travelling up with from Kumasi, and they were firmly in charge of the various market businesses and enterprises. They ran their business; setting prices, bartering and arguing the price of everything they had on sale. They would generally do this sitting on their haunches at the apex of their stall, often feeding a baby on one breast at the same time.

Exploring the town, I found myself walking into the Public Library, a largely empty building with a rather modest supply of books which had been provided mostly by the British Council. Straight in front of me were a number of shelves of reference books, which looked more interesting than the rest on offer. My eye caught the spine of a large book bound in brown leather entitled *Sir Gordon Guggisberg*. I'd heard a bit about this man. I sat down at a table in the

library and started to read about him. Although a professional soldier, he had also been director of public works on
the Gold Coast. But on the outbreak of the European war,
he re-joined the army and reached distinguished ranks,
including commanding the Royal Engineers during the
Battle of the Somme.

Following the First World War, in 1919 (by now Brigadier-
General Sir Frederick Gordon Guggisberg, K.C.M.G., D.S.O.,
R.E.) Guggisberg was appointed governor and commander-
in-chief of the Gold Coast. He was the man with the white
plumed hat, His Majesty's representative on this part of
African soil. He had become the most powerful man in a
country – a region – which had not chosen him, let alone
voted for him. The view of the empire I had then is the one
I still have today: in essence I believe it was like all other
imperialist regimes from Rome onwards, an inexcusable
exercise in exploitation and subjugation, however well-
intentioned and benign many of those that went out in its
name might have been.

But Guggisberg was different. He had thrown himself
above all into bettering the lot of the people he commanded
in this part of the West African coast. He was responsible
for many public projects, having extended the railways
and built the deep-water harbour on the coast at Sekondi-
Takoradi – essential to establishing the export-led cocoa
trade for Ghana, as it was to become – as well as founding
the Korle Bu Teaching Hospital in the capital Accra and,
perhaps his biggest legacy, the Achimota School. The college

was the seed from which grew many professional, political and administrative leaders in what is now Ghana. These included the first prime minister and president of Ghana, the late Kwame Nkrumah, as well as doctors, teachers, barristers and judges. Politicians, civil servants and engineers, all came out of the institution of Achimota founded by Guggisberg. The people not only admired Guggisberg but they came to love him for what he had achieved and the progress which he won for the country in his relatively short tenure of just over one decade as Governor-General.

Having read the introduction to the biography of this man, I started to flip through the rest of book. A page near the end of the biography fell open to reveal a black-and-white photograph. I blinked as I read the caption below it: 'The mayor Alderman F. B. Bending and the town councillors of Bexhill-on-Sea welcoming the Asantehene and his retinue at Bexhill Central Station in 1930.' I could not believe what I was seeing. There, in a small public library in a northern town of Ghana – on the road to Ouagadougou in Upper Volta, the country now known as Burkina Faso, which leads on to Timbuktu (best known as a metaphor for a distant or outlandish place) in the country of Mali – I had come across, by pure chance, a photograph of my paternal grandfather, who somehow had been part of this man's story. I made myself comfortable, opened the book at the section the photo referred to and read on avidly.

It turns out that Sir Gordon Guggisberg, having completed his hard-working and productive term of office in the

Gold Coast, had sailed off from Takoradi Harbour, which he had founded, to cheers of appreciation from crowds of well-wishers. He had retired to Bexhill in East Sussex where he had lived out his remaining days until he died on 21 April 1930 at the age of sixty. The description of his death was a sad one. He had died alone and in poverty, found dead by his neighbour at his home in Canterlupe Road (the road where the school I had attended – Pendragon School – was when I first joined it), propped up in bed wearing his Achimota School blazer and cap. Intestate, he was buried unceremoniously in a unmarked public grave in the Bexhill Highwoods Borough Cemetery.

When the people of his former colony somehow got to hear about the death of Guggisberg, they were shocked and upset. The Asantehene, the ruler of Kumasi and king of the Ashanti tribe, then the biggest dynasty in sub-Saharan Africa, set out with his royal retinue to correct the record. No mean feat for a group of tribal people who had never before travelled outside their own country, let alone by boat and train to a foreign continent.

The black-and-white photograph which I had first chanced across in Tamale Library showed the Asantehene in his ceremonial robes (gold and green in real life) standing on Bexhill station platform surrounded by his royal entourage, the men holding the royal ceremonial umbrella which was carried above the King everywhere he went and was the Sovereign's banner of honour. My grandfather is shown standing on the station platform in a black morning suit, his top hat under his left arm, bowing deeply in front of the King and offering his outstretched right hand in welcome to him and his royal party on behalf of the town and its council. The town clerk, aldermen and councillors, all similarly attired, are lined up behind him.

I don't know how much notice Grandfather and his colleagues might have had of this extraordinary visitation. I'm sure that it must have been a deeply unusual experience for them all and a talking point for years to come. The royal party made its way from Bexhill Central Station up to the Highwoods Borough Cemetery to pay homage to their beloved Governor-General at his burial place. Finding an unmarked pauper's grave, they made haste to correct this, the sole purpose for their long and devoted journey.

As soon as I returned to England, I took a trip to the Highwoods Cemetery. Up the hill on the right-hand side still stands plot number 114. It is now marked by a marble tombstone. The headstone is not grandiose and is weathered by the years, but dignified. The inscription reads:

To the Everlasting Memory of Governor Sir
Gordon Guggisberg who died in 1930 at Bexhill.
This memorial was erected by the Paramount
Chiefs and People of the Gold Coast and Ashanti.

Perhaps, after all, not everything about the empire was entirely bad?

In 1973, the year that I visited Ghana to work on the medical student elective in Accra, but unknown to me at the time, the Ghanaian government honoured Guggisberg with the erection of a large statue in his memory to commemorate the fiftieth anniversary of the construction of Korle Bu Hospital in Accra. The dedication of the statue took place a year later with its ceremonial unveiling by the then president of Ghana, Acheampong. The statue can still be seen to this day, situated at the front of the hospital's old administration building. Looking back, this was a rare tribute paid by a post-colonial government to one of its colonial governors.

II

Learning to Prescribe Drugs

WHILE IT IS TRUE THAT MOST PHYSICIANS DO NOT 'STICK anything in' or 'cut anything out', they do have one important role: that of understanding, appraising and effectively prescribing drugs. Having obtained a BSc honours degree in pharmacology (the study of drugs) before becoming a clinical medical student, this was a subject which had always particularly interested me. But a detailed knowledge of drugs and the prescribing of drugs is something which, I have to say, physicians in general are up-to-date and good at. Perhaps it is precisely because of the very fact that many of them cannot offer to 'stick anything in' or 'cut anything out'.

Obtaining a detailed record of what drugs a patient is taking, and has taken in the past, is an important part of taking a full history of that patient's problem and their presenting illness. Having said this, it does very often surprise me that so many of my medical colleagues do not seem to adhere to this dictum – and I don't just mean surgeons! They take notes and write letters in which no mention at all is made of the patient's list of prescribed drugs. Or, if they do feature, there may be a list of drug names (generic or proprietary) with no reference to the doses, frequency and timing and the patient's possible adherence to prescribed drug regimens. Likewise, taking note of any allergies or adverse side effects a patient may have suffered, and the nature of the side effects experienced, is also essential to taking a good history, to getting to know the patient. The list of drugs prescribed should also be checked with the patient's GP, since the prescription may have changed since the patient was referred to the hospital. Sadly, a significant percentage of referral letters from general practitioners to hospital specialists still include no reference to the patient's prescribed drug history, even though this can be printed out automatically from their record.

It is obvious, but not always remembered by doctors, that drugs should only be prescribed when necessary. A good analogy is that of surgery: it is wise not to operate unless the patient will benefit from you doing so. Even then, the benefit of prescribing a drug has to be weighed against the possible risks. All drugs have side effects, some of which do not become evident for a given patient until after the drug has been prescribed. The most well-known example of this is that of an allergy to an antibiotic, which is not apparent until the allergy occurs. Other side effects may take months or even years to develop.

It is also important for all doctors to discuss with a patient why he/she is prescribing a drug for them and to obtain their agreement with this. Sadly, although we always think we have done this – both in general practice and in hospital medicine – the truth is often otherwise. The prescription is much less likely to be effective if the patient has no idea what it is all about ('I don't know why I am being prescribed this'). Poor compliance often occurs because the purpose of the drug prescription has not been made clear; the perceived lack of efficiency of a drug not explained; the occurrence of a real or perceived side effect of a drug not discussed (it is astonishing how often patients blame the symptoms of their disease on the drug that they have been prescribed to control that disease); or because the beneficial effects of a drug might be expected to be delayed (e.g. the prescription of blood pressure-lowering drugs which may need to be taken for twenty years to significantly reduce the risk of suffering a stroke).

The prescribing of any drug by a doctor, therefore, has to start with obtaining the patient's agreement as to what health outcomes they wish to achieve and the strategy for achieving this. But this whole process does take time; sadly something which hospital doctors and general practitioners are strapped for. In modern-day jargon this is sometimes referred to as 'concordance', rather than simple compliance. (While a senior registrar on the Diabetes Unit at Guy's Hospital, my boss Professor Harry Keen once said to me, 'Don't use that word "compliant" in my clinic, Jeremy! You're not "compliant", I'm not "compliant"!!' He was right: indeed it's human nature to be 'non-compliant' with life in general, and with medical advice in particular.)

When it comes down to it, it is always about under-standing where your doctor is coming from, and that he / she, and his / her advice, is there to help. I often tackled this issue by making it clear that I would never prescribe a drug to any of my patients that I would not give to a member of my own family (or in the case of hypertension, one that I wasn't taking myself!). In the final analysis, I would never go ahead and prescribe a drug if I thought a patient was still not happy to take it or had not accepted the need for so doing: I knew very well that the tablets would likely not be swallowed (and flushed down the loo) or, if they were taken, would be less likely to be effective.

As a medical student, when the time for qualification was near (the certificate 'to kill or to cure' nearly upon us), the complexities of prescribing became real and more and more concerning. I was given a few simple rules, which remained helpful over my entire career and which I passed on to those that I subsequently trained. These included the dicta 'do not prescribe a drug unless you understand how it works'; 'start your career by sticking to prescribing a limited number of drugs (say, twenty – one in each class of drugs; there are so many examples of drugs in a single class, all having more or less the same effects, and side effects), so that you become familiar with those drugs and their effects to begin with'; 'examine the drug chart of every patient every time you see them (which should be a basic part of a ward round or clinic consultation)'; and 'be as ready to delete drugs previously prescribed as to prescribe new ones'. As a house officer I had a senior registrar who never thought he had completed a proper ward round unless he had deleted at least one drug from each patient's drug chart. This was good therapeutics and vitally important in avoiding 'polypharmacy' – the prescription of an unnecessary number of drugs – especially with the elderly. When patients are discharged from hospital with a list of drugs, it is amazing how often 'them out there' (GPs, practice and district nurses) assume that these always need to be continued in the long term. Patients often end up being prescribed them, sometimes incorrectly, for many years because of this trusting but unquestioning approach.

It is also well known that people with chronic conditions who are well (i.e. asymptomatic) do not continue to swallow their prescribed tablets after a period of time precisely *because* they are feeling well. Studies suggest that this may apply to sixty per cent or more of long-term prescriptions. They are flushed down the loo. A huge unnecessary cost to the health service, running into millions of pounds a year. This takes us back to the requirement that prescriptions be explained and drugs prescribed only as part of an agreed contract between the patient and prescribing doctor.

While we are considering the role of the physician as a prescriber, the wider issue of treatment in the Western world is an interesting one. I can remember, when on student elective in West Africa, learning that many African patients remained convinced that drugs given by mouth were always less effective than ones delivered by injection. To put it crudely, a bum full of injected antibiotics was thought to work better than tablets or capsules given orally – so much so that the offer of a course of tablets was often declined as being inferior and therefore not acceptable. This may indeed have been the case in situations where an on-going prescription could not be afforded or where the full course of an oral treatment was not adhered to.

In contrast to this attitude is the common lack of under-standing in our developed world that drugs alone may be only part of disease management. To put it simply, it is assumed that 'treatment equals drugs'. And in reverse: 'no drugs equals no treatment'. This is at its most taxing when, particularly in dealing with chronic diseases, the challenge is to persuade the patient with the condition of the need to take some responsibility for managing their disease themselves. In my experience, people are often not that impressed with being sent away with an exhortation to take more exercise, lose some weight (not the same thing), change their diet, aim to quit smoking, etc., etc., but without an immediate prescription to go with this advice. This in spite of the fact that to prescribe drugs immediately and early on may indeed be doing the patient no favours whatsoever and may actually negatively affect their long-term outcome.

Finally, the pressures on doctors to prescribe drugs are significant. And this does not only apply to the issue of patients expecting antibiotic prescriptions from their GP for common viruses such as a sore throat. This is a situation in which antibiotics are ineffective and the prescription of them in the past has been an important factor in the very worrying development of antibiotic-resistant bacteria, which has rightly been given much air time recently. I do understand what I call the 'prescription reflex': 'Here you are madam. Take this and get out of my hair!' But the pressure on a doctor to prescribe not only comes from patients themselves but also from their peers and the drug industry. I have always advised medical students close to qualifying and new doctors of their responsibility to eschew bribes – gifts, free meals, etc. In the past doctors were often wined and dined by drug companies, and not only in their own locality but also by means of costly domestic and international travel to conferences and meetings. The *British Medical Journal* front cover some years ago showing a cartoon of doctors as pigs with their noses in a trough caused much indignation – both from doctors and the drug industry – but rightly led to some curbing of this excess.

Nevertheless, drug representatives still lined up to sponsor the lunch for our weekly multidisciplinary team meetings with their company's educational budget, and put pressure on the more junior members of teams – senior house officers and registrars especially – to try out their drug. They would then maintain this pressure by following-up at later meetings and asking, 'How is X going?' or similar. Don't get me wrong, I know what pressures drug-company representatives remain under to justify their existence. Their ability to tick boxes for the number of doctors they have spoken to is one way their effectiveness is measured and continuing employment assessed. To be able to report back that consultant Y is now prescribing their drug (and therefore likely the rest of his/her team also) is a major coup. Some drug reps do have a background in science and higher degrees and are able to give a balanced overview of the pharmacology of a new compound which can be very helpful. But, to be honest, this is not the majority, and it was the rump that not only expressed their displeasure at my lack of willingness to immediately change my prescribing habits, but in fact often attempted to sideline my views in favour of my more junior colleagues, with the unspoken implication that I was an out-of-date luddite! I delighted in repeating the advice I was given myself before qualifying: 'Be conservative in your prescribing in your patients' best interests'; and 'don't prescribe a drug that you would not give to yourself or your own family'; and 'let the side effects of a drug become apparent in other doctors' patients first!' I have to say that not all my more junior doctor colleagues seemed impressed, peering as they were into their hand-held smart phones to look for prescribing guidance.

12

Sticking Things In

THERE ARE SOME GROUPS OF PHYSICIANS, OF COURSE, that do spend a lot of time 'sticking things in'. Take the 'electricians' and the 'plumbers', for example. The 'electricians' is how we often used to refer to our cardiologist (heart specialist) colleagues. The interventionist ones at least. They spend a lot of time passing small catheters into peoples' coronary arteries, down which they squirt dye. They are searching for evidence of blockages to the coronaries which can then either be stretched out (an angioplasty) and/or have a little expanding mesh (a stent) inserted to keep the vessel patent. If they find that your heart rate has become irregular, they might fry your atrium (that chamber of the heart where the rhythm's loss of control has occurred) with multiple little explosive shocks in an attempt to re-establish normal cardiac rhythm. If your heart has lost its normal rhythm because the wiring within it has worn out (causing a marked slowing down of the heart rate, or 'heart block') and needs replacing, no problem. In that case they will pop a little junction box into your chest wall (a cardiac pacemaker), from which they can thread a wire or two into the main chambers of the heart to bring the heartbeat back to a synchronised normal speed. If you are lucky they will add in at no extra charge (to yourself at least; thank goodness that in our National Health Service treatment is still free at the point of delivery, unlike the US of A, where all that would clean you out to the tune of perhaps hundreds of thousands of dollars) an electric defibrillator, which will shock your heart back into action should it be inconsiderate enough to decide to stop beating. Anyway, that's my little synopsis of what these operating physician electricians do with their days.

Although cardiologists are required to spend a great deal of their days working as electricians, involved in undertaking these procedures, they do also treat people with established heart failure medically as well, of course, and run clinics in which they see patients. They are also referred patients with problems not just of the heart, but with other disorders of the circulatory system, such as high blood pressure (hypertension). Although I am sure many of my cardiology colleagues would object, I believe that, in general, cardiologists are usually not that much interested in high blood pressure. They generally seem to view the subject as less exciting than catheters and pacemakers and so on. Unless, of course, they are asked to see a patient privately with severe hypertension which has been resistant to blood pressure-lowering drug treatment and there may be the need for a new 'interventional' technique called renal artery ablation, which is still very much unproven.

There are many causes of high blood pressure and some of the most interesting causes (although perhaps rather rare) turn out to be secondary to diseases of the hormone glands (endocrine diseases) or kidneys (renal disease). I therefore always advise that if you have developed hypertension, the person you should choose to see is either an endocrinologist or a nephrologist (kidney specialist). I practised what I preached, relying on my good friend who is a nephrologist for help and advice about the treatment of my own high blood pressure. I was fairly recently asked to see a patient with very high blood pressure by his GP for a second opinion. The man's blood pressure remained persistently high and resistant to all the blood pressure-lowering drugs that were thrown at him. The patient had been attending the cardiology clinic at our hospital for some years (and had nearly always been seen by a junior doctor), during which time nobody had called for the simple test of dipping a stick into his urine for analysis. On his first visit to see me in my clinic the urinalysis showed large amounts of microscopic blood and protein in his urine and the cause of his raised blood pressure turned out to be secondary to an underlying chronic kidney condition.

The 'plumbers', or gastroenterologists, are equally busy 'sticking things in'. They spend many happy hours looking down from the mouth to examine your stomach (upper GI endoscopy), or up your anus to look at your large bowel (colonoscopy), with their fibre-optic endoscopes (or 'liquorice sticks' as I call them, because that's what the flexible

shiny black 'scopes look like). To their credit, these camer-
aman gastroenterologists (or 'hollow organ endoscopists',
as they are also sometimes referred to) have stolen a bit of
a march on their surgical colleagues. They are able to sort
out a good deal of problems and pathologies that in the
past could only be achieved by a surgeon opening up your
abdomen to have a look inside. In turn, however, some of
the procedures that they would have done half a dozen or
so of before lunch have now been taken over by our interventional radiologist friends. These include things like liver
biopsies; taking a snip of liver tissue to look at under the
microscope in order to determine the cause of the disease
affecting the function of the liver. Since it was agreed that
the risks of this procedure – bleeding or leaking bile into
the abdomen – were infrequent but significant, these days
if you require a biopsy of your liver you will most likely find
yourself being wheeled down to the X-ray department to
have a radiologist (X-ray specialist) perform the procedure
under either ultrasound or CT-scan guidance.

During my first six months as a house physician after
qualifying as a doctor, I remember being required to perform liver biopsies on my own, including on patients whose
abdominal cavity may have been full of fluid (ascites), when
the risks of bleeding and/or leakage of bile from the liver
are considerably higher. On reflection, this approach was
no more precise than what we used to call 'apple bobbing'
when we were kids: the challenge of having to bend over a
large bucket of water full of apples with your hands behind

your back and try to get a bite of one, if you can remember playing that game on Halloween? While I never experienced any untoward occurrences when performing this task – as far as I know! – performing a liver biopsy under CT-scan guidance, as is common practice these days, is safer for the patient I am sure. It is, however, just one example of the fact that there are less and less practical experiences to be had for doctors in training these days.

13

Seat of Academe

WHILE I WAS WORKING AS AN SHO ON THE INTENSIVE Therapy Unit at Charing Cross Hospital in London, I passed the membership examination of the Royal College of Physicians. This was a necessary passport if one wanted to progress in a career of specialist hospital medicine. After working for eight months on the Charing Cross ITU, I stayed on there to do a number of locum medical registrar posts. The next substantive post I was appointed to was as medical registrar to the Professorial Medical Unit at Addenbrooke's Hospital in Cambridge. I was proud to have obtained this post and was looking forward immensely to extending my training in both the theory and practice of medicine. I was also anticipating the intellectual challenge that I was certain would be found within the academic milieu of the seat of academe that is Cambridge University.

I was not disappointed by the amount and diversity of medicine there was to be learnt at Addenbrooke's. As well as being a leading university teaching hospital, Addenbrooke's also served as the main regional hospital for a large population covering a sizeable swathe of East Anglia and eastern England. So, unlike some traditional teaching units, there was a very busy service commitment to be sustained. It was, therefore, an opportunity for me to experience a wide range of both emergency and routine medicine. The emergency rotas were very busy, and I saw large numbers of patients admitted. In addition to this were the busy medical outpatient clinics. For the first time in my career, I learnt how to run an outpatient clinic and the importance of starting on time and keeping to time. This is no mean feat when, in between the more straight-forward cases, one has to spend a lot of time with a patient to whom one has to break bad news, for example. It is a challenge to ensure that all patients are given as much time as they need, while not keeping others waiting. The hope is that all the patients whom one sees will go away feeling that they have been listened to and have obtained a plan of investigation and treatment for their problem which they are happy with. This art is an important one to acquire and has to be learnt through experience. My experience of the seat of academe, however, also included something of a disappointment. The reason for this was the senior bosses for whom I was working.

The professor of medicine, Professor Henry Grant, was an intelligent man – you are not rewarded with the chair of medicine at such a prestigious university if this is not the case – and clinically I found him a supportive boss. He was a good example of a listening doctor, carefully paying attention to his patients and colleagues, including myself, on his ward rounds. He had, however, developed an intense, and some might have said disproportionate, interest in the disease anorexia nervosa. This is a beastly condition, which affects young women almost exclusively, and is apparently a rather new disease: it certainly does not seem to have existed much before the middle of the twentieth century. It undoubtedly has some psychosocial aspects: we saw a procession of highly intelligent, high-achieving 'bluestocking' female undergraduates who had been afflicted by the condition. They very often had parents who were putting them under intense pressure to succeed, but who were also going through marital disharmony or breakup themselves at the same time, although they would not usually admit this to us. It is true that the condition does have some interesting endocrinological (hormonal) changes associated with it, but the evidence suggests that these are secondary to the condition rather than the cause of it. The professor appeared to have developed some rather alternative views on the subject of anorexia, however, and was prone to writing at length in non-medical journals such as women's magazines. There was nothing wrong with this in itself, of course, but it gave him a reputation of having gone off the academic rails somewhat. There was a story that his obsession with 'AN' derived from the fact that he had a daughter who had been severely afflicted by the disease. If this was right, then I had sympathy for him. It was also clear that he did have a cussed side to him, which I am sure he exhibited in his dealings with his senior colleagues and when chairing committees.

My other consultant boss was the senior lecturer, a lady called Dr Jane Williams, who was a highly intelligent woman. She was definitely not a listening doctor, however. She was charming when we met together socially, but professionally she was excessively highly strung, a characteristic which impacted negatively on her ability to relate to both patients and colleagues alike. She would spend a long time looking at the notes and discussing the details of each patient's blood chemistry, but when she got to the end of their bed she did not really seem able to relate to the sick patient and their problems, leaving many of them bewildered and still needing help and advice. The result of this was that, following her ward round, I usually had to do a round of all the patients we had just seen to explain what had been said and what the implications and plans for their illnesses and treatments were.

These characteristics were nothing to do with the fact that Dr Williams was a woman; but like Prime Minister Margaret Thatcher at the time, she seemed to exist on almost no sleep. When I was on call as Dr Williams's registrar, I might call her in the middle of the night at 3 a.m. to let her know about a sick patient I had just admitted (she always insisted on keeping things on a short piece of string and wanted to know about all the patients who had been admitted, as if she did not really trust her more junior team members) to find that she would still be wide awake and working.

Whatever the personal characteristics of my two consultant bosses, one thing was quite clear on a daily basis. And
that was that they despised each other. Dr Williams would
shout and scream at the professor in public – I remember
her almost foaming at the mouth in clinical seminars as she
threw X-rays on the ground and jumped up and down on
them in disagreement with what he had said. For his part,
it was obvious Professor Henry Grant held 'this intelligent
but histrionic young lady' in great disdain and took some
pleasure in digging his heels in and opposing everything
his female colleague wished to propose. On more than
one occasion I can remember Dr Williams grabbing me by
the arm as she dragged me away right in the middle of the
professor's ward round. 'You've had him long enough! He's
mine now!!' she would cry. It is difficult enough serving more
than one master in any professional role, but the intensity
of the loathing between my two bosses made life almost
impossible to bear at times. As a result of this experience, I
vowed that when I became a consultant physician myself,
I would never require my registrar to work between two
bosses, a vow I am pleased to say I was able to maintain.

14

Listening in a Different Language?

I RECEIVED A TELEPHONE CALL OUT OF THE BLUE ONE morning: 'Dr Bending? This is Cyril Galway calling.'

'Yes?' I replied.

'Cyril Galway, from the Department of Health, Newfoundland.' The telephone line was crackling and his voice was fading in and out. 'When can you start?'

'Oh, right,' I said, suddenly remembering what this was all about. In the uncertainty and disappointment of life in the professorial academic Department of Medicine at Addenbrooke's Hospital in Cambridge I had sent off my CV to the Department of Health in Newfoundland, Canada enquiring about the possibility of a job in the 'outports', as the coastal fishing towns were called. My friend Roger was working there with his wife Peta at the time and had suggested that I go over too, at least for a short break. 'It might help you to look at things from a different perspective,' Roger had said to me on the phone in a well-meaning way. 'I've found that looking at life from the other side of the pond has been a way to help me decide where I want to go next.' It sounded like a good idea. It would take me away from the seat of academe and give me the chance to reassess what I wanted to do for the rest of my career. It would be an opportunity to decide whether I really did wish to pursue a career in hospital medicine.

It was four in the morning and I was still wrestling with cardboard boxes and Sellotape, trying desperately to finish the packing-up of our personal belongings before our little house was to be let out while we were away. We had been married in the registry office on Castle Hill in Cambridge a few months before, and this was our first home together. We needed to let the place while we were away to help pay for the mortgage. My wife Jan was sitting on the stairs in tears. 'I don't want to go! This was all your idea!!' she was crying. I have to say that I was filled with the same uncertainty that she was and feared that I might be making a major error with this move, both professionally and personally. But I was too proud to admit the fact, and carried on packing. We were due to fly off from Heathrow Airport later that afternoon.

The Air Canada flight landed at St John's, the capital of the province of Newfoundland and Labrador. While waiting for our luggage to arrive on the carousel, I was able to wander round the little museum in the airport terminal which commemorated the first non-stop trans-atlantic crossing by plane, a feat undertaken by the British aviators Alcock and Brown in 1919. The distance from St John's, Newfoundland to Galway in Ireland was the short-est route across the Atlantic as the crow flies, and they had only just made it. We felt at the time that we were pioneers in the opposite direction, leaving home and family for the unknown. We were soon to find out that many of those living in Newfoundland were the descendants of migrants who had come east to west, in the same direction that we had, journeying by sea across the Atlantic Ocean from the West Country of England, Scotland or Ireland seeking a new life. The heritage which the 'Newfies' brought with them was to be found in the songs of the sea and the Celtic-flavoured country music which they still perform to this day. We were met at the airport by a taxi and driven the short distance to the Holiday Inn Hotel by the lake. After unpacking enough for the night, we stopped in at the hotel restaurant overlooking the lake and had a nice meal together, including Newfie fish chowder soup and local venison as well as a bottle of Californian wine. Things were looking up a little.

The next morning we caught a Provincial Airlines flight to a place called Stephenville Crossing on the west coast of the island of Newfoundland. As we looked down, we could see the forests and, scattered along the shores, the small 'outports' – the fishing towns and villages. In those days, Newfoundland had two staple industries. The first was the forestry trade and the logging that came from it. The other was the fisheries. Most of the men not involved in the logging trade were working in the fisheries, many of them going out on trawlers to fish the Grand Banks and the St Lawrence Seaway. Large numbers of the women worked in fish plants located in many of the small outport towns, where cod and other fish were filleted, frozen and packed. As the plane descended towards our landing I could see the vast Deer Lake out of the right-hand window, with its huge tree trunks floating on the water like scores of matchsticks and jostling together towards the river outlet. Later, from the ground, we were to watch men riding on the logs and guiding them towards the lake exits with their poles. Further north from Deer Lake, the immense mountains of Gros Morne National Park could be seen rising into the clouds.

The airport at Stephenville Crossing was about all there was to see when we landed, apart from the crossing that was! This small, remote community which had grown up on the west coast of Newfoundland had gained its name from being the spot where the Trans-Canada Highway intersects the road going up to the Northern Peninsula. We were met by a taxi driver, who loaded our bags into the back of his car and made us comfortable before we headed off down Highway Number One, the Trans-Canada Highway. The driver told us that we had a drive of about 120 miles ahead of us. A few miles west of Stephenville Crossing the taxi turned left off the Trans-Canada, heading south to the town of Burgeo, located on the south coast of the island of Newfoundland. The way from there was not made up – 'without pavement', as they say in North America – and we bumped about the rock-strewn muddy road as the driver weaved left and right, choosing the best parts and avoiding the potholes as best he could. The land was more or less tundra, apart from the fir forest covering the higher parts of the hills. 'Do you come down this way often?' I asked our driver.

'Nope,' came his reply. 'Fact is, never been down to Burgeo before in my life!' Jan and I looked at each other. Where were we going to?

After something like ninety miles of unmade track full of humps and potholes, the surface eventually started to improve and then finally became made up with asphalt. When we neared Burgeo, the road followed a number of sharp bends as it started its descent towards the southern shore of the island. Through the pine trees we caught our first glimpse of the icy sea. When we reached the small town of Burgeo, with its wooden multi-coloured dwellings distributed on the granite rocks, the taxi left us and our luggage at the door of the small Cottage Hospital.

The hospital was operated by the Department of Health and run by two married Scottish GPs and a third assistant doctor, which was to be me. We received a warm welcome from the RNs – registered nurses – who were enjoying supper in the kitchen when we arrived, which consisted of a fish 'scoff'. They offered us some and when we were finished the chief nurse Patsy showed us to our living accommodation. This turned out to be in a 'trailer' which was actually a long caravan with no wheels that was permanently placed on the top of a small granite hillock just opposite the hospital. Pretty convenient for work, you might think, until the deep winter snow drifts arrived. I can well remember one night on call having to struggle for about thirty minutes to get out of the trailer and across the road to the hospital, which was covered in drifts of snow some feet high. The trailer had two floors and a door leading straight out of one of the bedrooms at first-floor level, just like all of the other houses and trailers in the area, so that one could walk out of the bedroom into the snow when it reached that high and had blocked the ground floor completely.

I very soon got into the routine of Cottage Hospital life. I was essentially working as an intern for the long-established Scottish man-and-wife partners who ruled the place. Anne, the dominant partner, ruled the town in more than just the medical sense. She was the mayor and clearly saw herself as the town's matriarch. Her husband Mike was a laid back – lazy? – pipe-smoking partner who seemed to come and go as he pleased, which appeared to be not very often to the hospital and clinics. In spite of their long-term tenure, I soon became aware that I knew a considerable amount more up-to-date medicine than they did, although they did not seem ready to acknowledge this fact. My clinics became more like consultant specialist medicine sessions, rather than general practice, although I did my best to cope with all the other demands of family medicine, including gynaecology and paediatrics, which were areas I had hitherto not been called upon to address in my career. I got a lot of satisfaction in finding out that the reason why our male social worker's wife was experiencing repeated miscarriages was because she had a congenital abnormality of her womb – a bi-cornuate ('double-horned') uterus, which gave insufficient space for the developing foetus to hang on to as it grew larger. This was cured by a referral to a gynaecologist in St John's, who was able to reverse the problem by means of fairly simple reconstructive surgery, refashioning the lady's uterus.

One of the earliest challenges I had to grapple with was to learn the local Newfie language. A woman would come into the clinic and sit down. 'What's the problem, Beth?' I would ask. 'I find's me stomach, doctor,' would come the reply. This turned out to mean that the patient was experiencing dyspepsia or even abdominal pains. My wife Jan – who had not wanted to come on this trip! – was really enjoying her new life as an RN at the Cottage Hospital, now that she had got into the swing of things. For one thing, the other nurses accepted her on to the team without hesitation and she found them all to be very friendly, once she had got used to the flapping of Betsy, the most senior nurse, who was a well-meaning ex-nun underneath. One of the particular joys Jan was exposed to was that of delivering babies. When I came home early one day and told Jan about some of the problems I had been having understanding the Newfie language, she told me how the fifteen-year-old girl whose baby she had delivered that morning had asked for the phone trolley to phone her mum. 'Hi, Ma!' Darleen had cried into the phone. 'I got better at eight o'clock!!' as if her pregnancy had been an illness rather than a phys-iological occurrence. Teenage pregnancy in the outports was no different than at home – and probably even more common. In spite of the charm and quaintness of the place, we both very soon came to learn that this also applied to the occurrence of drug- and alcohol-fuelled social disloca- tion, which was no less common than in the big cities in Canada and the UK.

15

Listen to the Wind!

ON TUESDAY EVENINGS IN BURGEO I WOULD SIT IN our trailer listening with even more attention than usual to the wind howling outside. The reason for this was that early every Wednesday morning it was my duty to take the ferry out to the island of Ramea to conduct a clinic at the nursing station there. Being a poor sailor, I would dread the arrival of Wednesday mornings. Ramea Island was only about ten miles off the coast from Burgeo, but the journey was almost always a rough one. The ferry which ploughed back and forth was called the *Senator Penny*, a name which it had brought with it from the East Coast of the USA, where it had started its life, before being retired out to ply the crossing from Burgeo to Ramea. Now pretty aged and infirm, the rusty round-bottomed hull did nothing to protect its passengers from the severe buffeting it would receive at the hands of storms in the St Lawrence Seaway. It would pitch, yaw and roll backwards and forwards on every cross-ing: even in the summer months but especially during the bitter storms in the winter, which in practice usually meant at least eight months in a year. In spite of the relatively short distance which it had to traverse, the ferry took at least an hour to cross the angry water, even on a good day.

As I stood on the Government Wharf waiting for the ferry to arrive to carry me over to Ramea Island on my first visit, I received a friendly nod from Jed Strickland, a young man in his early twenties with a shock of curly red hair who lived in the next trailer down the hill from us. Jed was an electrician who worked for Newfoundland Power and travelled over to Ramea on a regular basis to inspect the electricity substations or repair the supply from a power cable which had been blown down in the most recent set of storms. I gave him a sheepish smile back and climbed aboard the *Senator Penny* as she docked alongside the wharf. I went straight down below and found myself a long seat covered with a rubber mat which I was able to lie out flat on. I had learnt in the past that lying flat on my side, and as still as possible, was a good way to avoid seasickness, if one possibly could. I therefore adopted this anti-social position every time I was required to take the ferry over to Ramea. The need to avoid vomiting, if at all possible, meant that I was not able to join in the talk and laughter of the other passengers, and therefore missed an opportunity to get to know them better, especially the regulars. As I looked up lamely, I was aware of one or two of my fellow passengers giving a sympathetic smile in my direction.

All my life I have been prone to seasickness. Indeed, as a child I used to develop 'seasickness' even when riding on a swing boat in the fair, as well as the inevitable car sickness on any journey longer than a short trip. When driving in the car on our annual family summer holiday from the South Coast of England to Scotland or the Lake District, it was taken for granted that 'Jeremy will be car sick' after we had reached only about an hour into the journey. It was always assumed by my parents and siblings that this had something to do with my being over-excited about the holiday ahead. As I got older, and still remained prone to seasickness, I realised that it had nothing to do with 'emotion' but everything to do with motion.

It was during my time in Newfoundland that I learnt that motion sickness seems to be something which is genetically inherited, perhaps to do with a hypersensitivity to motion of the inner ear? When I got to know the men who regularly went out fishing for a living, they told me that it was just accepted that some men vomited in response to motion sickness and some did not. I learnt that there were captains of cod fishing trawlers who always vomited for the first few days of the ten or so spent out on a fishing trip. And these were men, some of whom were in their sixties, who had been making their living as trawler men since they took up their trade at the age of fourteen or fifteen. In other words, even after about fifty years of spending their lives working on the sea, they had not been able to rid themselves of the unpleasantness of seasickness.

As the *Senator Penny* finally docked at the wharf on Ramea Island, I struggled up on deck, having one last vomit into the scuppers as I did so. I looked up from the gangway to see a short man in his fifties, with a cheery smile from ear to ear, beaming down at me as he held out his hand to help the 'new doctor' up on to the quay. He turned out to be Douglas Stewart, the Glasgow-born registered nurse who ran the nursing station on Ramea Island. He had emigrated with his wife Barbara after the war, leaving Scotland behind them for a new life in Canada and Newfoundland where they had remained since. They were devoted to their role in this remote island outport community and Douglas, as well as running the Ramea Nursing Station, was also responsible for other small island and mainland coastal communities, with names like La Poile, Grand Bruit, Muddy Hole, Grey River and François. He would regularly take his life in his hands by setting out in his small motor boat – sometimes in violent storms in the middle of the night – to help the sick and women in labour.

After giving me his hand to haul me up on to the quay, Douglas introduced himself and gave me a few minutes to gain my land legs and banish the sickness. He then walked me up the hill to the nursing station where his wife Barbara was waiting excitedly to welcome the new doctor. I could see that there was already a line of some ten or twelve people waiting patiently outside the front door to the clinic. We went inside, where Douglas showed me around and went through the, pretty basic, equipment they had to offer. Barbara ran a small pharmacy from a little room next to the clinic, from where she dispensed any prescriptions I might wish to write. Once I had got the rundown, I sat down in the consulting room to start the clinic. I could see in the mirror that I was looking decidedly green around the gills and was aware as I sat there that I was gripping the desk with white knuckles as if I was still being tossed around on the ferry.

Douglas showed the first patient in to my clinic and sat him down at the desk next to me. He was a man old enough to be my father. 'Are you all right, doctor?' was the first thing the patient said, peering closely at me, clearly more concerned with the health of the new doctor than he was about whatever ailment he needed to consult me for. Both Douglas and I burst out laughing, and the patient followed suit. From then on, the clinic progressed steadily and with good humour.

At 12.30, Barbara strode in to the room politely but firmly announcing that she had closed the clinic for the morning, regardless of how many people there may have been still waiting – they would be required to return after the 'doctor has had his lunch'. Douglas was a Glaswegian who had been born and brought up in the Gorbals. Barbara, for her part, was a lady who was 'Yorkshire through and through'. Her hospitality was always without question and one aspect of this was her determination to 'feed the doctor a good lunch'. This usually involved a huge plate of home-made steak and kidney pie with carrots and mashed potatoes, or some other stew she had been preparing since the night before. This would be followed by one of Barbara's suet puddings, such as spotted dick and custard. I was always too polite to refuse, but would sit at the dining-room table listening to the wind getting up and watching the white caps on the increasingly large waves through the panoramic bay window as the weather took a change for the worse. I knew that Barbara's steak and kidney pie would come straight back up again not long after I had got back on the ferry for the trip back to Burgeo and the mainland. But I was not allowed to decline her hospitality and was usually pressed to help myself to a second serving. After a number of miserable Wednesday journeys back from the Ramea clinic, I started to get canny: if I happened to come across a patient who was ill enough to need admission to the Burgeo Cottage Hospital, or even onward to the regional hospitals in Corner Brook or St John's, I would have no choice but to radio in for a helicopter to take me and my patient quickly, and relatively smoothly, back to the mainland, wouldn't I?

I got to love Doug and Barbara and admired them enormously for their absolute devotion to duty and to the peoples of Ramea Island and the other outports along the south coast of Newfoundland which Douglas had responsibility for. My admiration for them was made greater from time to time by an awareness that the people they served mostly had no understanding of how lucky they were to have such a devoted professional couple in their midst. This is not to say that Douglas's ability and training were always sufficient to answer the calls he received for help. He was only an RN who had trained in Glasgow in the 1940s, after all, and not a doctor, surgeon or obstetrician, which the situations he was put in frequently required him to be. Occasionally I was momentarily frustrated by his medical naïvety, but I never forgot the background from which he was operating, nor could I blame him for not doing his best.

I particularly remember one dark, stormy November night when Douglas phoned me at 3 a.m. on his walkie talkie in undisguised panic to say he had been called out on his boat to a woman in Grand Bruit (pronounced 'Grand Brit'), a little community along the coast west of Ramea, to find that she was in obstructed labour when he arrived. There was not very much I could do to help him over the phone, except give him encouragement and support. I was standing waiting for him on the Government Wharf at 5 a.m. when a small motor boat came chugging in out of the fog and lashing rain to reveal Douglas at the wheel in his orange storm gear with his sou'wester pulled firmly down over his eyes. I jumped on to the boat and went straight to the cabin. The mother was alive and did survive. However, her dead baby was hanging half in and half out between her legs. I gave the Mum an oxytocin injection and delivered the dead child there in the boat. It was all very sad.

I am pleased to say that shortly before his retirement Douglas was awarded the Order of Canada by the Canadian government for the services he had delivered to the people in this remote part of Newfoundland. Sadly, he died from lung cancer not long after he retired, a result of his life-long heavy smoking habit.

16

Listening at an Open Door

AFTER A FEW MONTHS THE WORK AS A JUNIOR GENERAL
practitioner, while wearing a physician's hat, started to feel
insufficiently challenging. Whilst our adventure to the outports of Newfoundland had made a fascinating change, it had
helped me to decide that I did want to continue my career
in specialist hospital medicine. The question then arose: in
which country and in which specialty should I seek to practise?

I received another telephone call out of the blue. This
time, to be precise, there were two calls. One was from the
Charles S. Curtis Memorial Hospital in St Anthony, on the
northern tip of Newfoundland, asking me if I could stand in
for one month as locum consultant physician for their consultant who was to go on sabbatical. The other was from Dr
Barry May, the consultant chest physician from the Western
Memorial Regional Hospital in Corner Brook, the second
city of Newfoundland. A British doctor, Dr Brian Harley,
their consultant in diabetes and endocrinology, had gone off
on sick leave, apparently seriously ill, and they were looking
for someone to stand in for him. Barry gave me a telephone

interview. He understood that I was a member of the Royal College of Physicians, whose diploma examination I had passed, and had been medical registrar to the professor of medicine at Cambridge, where I had gained specialist experience in diabetes and endocrinology? My answer to this was, 'Yes,' to which he replied, 'When can you start?' I explained that I would have to give notice for my present GP contract in Burgeo and honour the month locum I had just committed to in St Anthony. He was happy to wait for me to start after this.

My month spent up in St Anthony, on the tip of the Northern Peninsula of Newfoundland, working as a locum consultant physician was extremely enjoyable. The patients I had to look after were all very interesting, not least because the sick ones had usually been flown in by fixed-wing sea plane from one of the nursing stations up the coast. Sir Wilfred Grenfell, the hospital's founder, had been an English missionary doctor who had established health care through- out the northern part of the province, not least setting up nursing stations at regular intervals the whole way up the remote Labrador coast. These nursing stations were almost all run by highly experienced nurses, SRNs from Scotland and other parts of the United Kingdom and Canada. They almost all practised alone, without any immediate help apart from advice on the radio from the hospital at St Anthony should they need it. This meant that they not only cared for, but were responsible themselves for treating patients with all sorts of medical and surgical emergencies. They often had no option, since not only might it be some days before their patients could be air-ambulanced out to St Anthony, but very often in the severe winter storms they were cut off indefinitely from help from the outside and just had to cope. One example of this, for instance, was that they would have no hesitation in treating a man who had just suffered a heart attack. If their patient's condition did deteriorate to the point where they had no choice but to send him in to us by air, the patient would inevitably arrive with a typed referral letter which included every detail of the patient's history, treatment and monitoring to date. I was immensely impressed by these nurses' ability to cope and by their competence. The letters they sent in with their patients were in general far superior to most GP referral letters one might receive in the UK.

My wife Jan would occasionally have the chance to visit one of the nursing stations up the Labrador coast by sea plane, usually during an obstetric emergency when she was required to bring a woman in complicated labour over to St Anthony. I still have a vivid memory of walking out of the hospital one afternoon to see Jan sitting on the shore in the evening sunshine, selling scallops to passers-by from a consignment she had picked up in Labrador on her way back from one such trip.

My time at the Western Memorial Regional Hospital in Corner Brook was a contrast, but equally stimulating. There were a number of internists (i.e. consultant physicians) working there, including Barry May (a Canadian chest physician),

Huw Jenkins (a Welsh gastroenterologist) and John Dancy (a Canadian haematologist). We shared the acute medicine on-call rota, had our own inpatients and also consulted from the 'office' – a suite of consulting rooms in the shopping mall in town, where outpatients were seen. There were no junior medical staff, so each internist would look after his patient in full from their admission to hospital until their discharge. I spent three months standing in for Dr Brian Harley, who was a British diabetologist and endocrinologist. I enjoyed this so thoroughly – particularly the D & E part of it – that the experience ended up helping me to make up my mind, just as my friend Roger had predicted it would when he encouraged me to go out for a spell in Newfoundland. The answers to my self-searching questions were: yes, I did want to continue a career in hospital medicine; and that diabetes and endocrinology was what I wanted to train to be a specialist in.

I had driven with Roger the hundreds of miles to St John's on the south-eastern tip of Newfoundland to sit the Canadian MB exam (the LMCC, or Licentiate of the Medical Council of Canada), which we both passed. The next question to be answered was: where should I seek to gain further training as a specialist? Jan and I had both enjoyed our year in Newfoundland and very much liked the Canadian way of life and, in particular, the Canadian people. In the end, however, the pull of family and friends brought us back to the UK to follow our dreams and my professional intentions here.

Nevertheless, I did not say goodbye to Newfoundland completely. I was to go back and work there again on half a dozen occasions after I had become a consultant physician in the UK. I would use my summer holiday to fly over to Newfie, often with my wife and kids in tow, to work as an internist at the G. B. Cross Hospital in Clarenville, central Newfoundland. They would pay a good salary – which helped with our UK mortgage payments at the time – as well as supply me with a car (usually from the car loan company Rent a Wreck, which in spite of the company name would more often than not provide a swish Chevrolet shooting brake) and appropriate rent-free accommodation. The latter would consist of a fully equipped house when Jan and the kids came with me. I did not mind working in my vacation. In any case, the work was not intense and it gave me the opportunity to sharpen up again at the basics, since, as had been the case when I had done consultant physician locum jobs in St Anthony and Corner Brook, I did not have any junior assistants and had to care for the patients entirely myself from admission to discharge. I could return to my consultant post in the UK having refreshed my experience at the workface, which enabled me to relate to my own junior staff in Eastbourne. Added to which, the holidays were really great fun for our young kids, who had the opportunity to visit the Terra Nova National Park; go looking for black bears up at the corporation refuse site out on the Trans-Canada Highway (staying safely in the car as we watched them coming to forage at the tip); and make trips out in the early misty mornings to get up close to the herds of moose on Random Island. We made many very good friends during our visits to Newfoundland and have kept in touch with them since.

17

'I'm Keen – Are You?'

So we returned to the UK, Jan and I, and for a few months I worked as a locum medical registrar (and on one occasion locum consultant) while I searched for a senior registrar specialist training post in diabetes and endocrinology. This entailed writing applications and sending my CV off to many of the main university teaching centres with a reputation for D & E. I was invited to visit centres in Oxford, Newcastle and London, among other places, where I received a polite audience and offers of the possibility of doing a research fellowship in each centre. Professor George Alberti in Newcastle-upon-Tyne kindly took me to lunch in the canteen and discussed the idea of him arranging a Wellcome research fellowship for me on his unit, which might take a few months to arrange. 'What do you think about coming to work in Newcastle?' George Alberti asked me.

'There's just one problem, professor' – Alberti spluttered into his plate of spaghetti bolognaise at the possibility that I was not eternally grateful for his offer – 'my mother-in-law lives here!' I replied with a big grin, before we both burst out laughing.

My last informal interview was on the Unit for Metabolic Medicine at Guy's Hospital in London, with Professor Harry Keen. At that time the unit had already built an outstanding reputation for itself and was one of the leading diabetes research units not only in the UK, but also in the world. I was welcomed by the friendly secretary Jean and ushered down the corridor to Professor Keen's office. I was surprised to find Harry Keen sitting at his desk and smoking a pipe in an office not much bigger than the cupboard under our stairs, an unexpectedly modest accommodation for the man I knew to be a world-famous diabetes expert. As Harry interviewed me, leaning forward benignly, I looked down to see the book of matches which he had been using to light his pipe sitting on the desk. On the cardboard cover was a personalised printed logo: 'I'm Keen – Are You?' The interview seemed to have gone pretty well and my answer to the challenge on Harry's matchbox was, 'I am *very* keen!' I was sent down the corridor to meet Dr John Pickup and Dr Giancarlo Viberti, two of the unit's research stars, whom I was equally impressed with. I really felt that this was somewhere I wanted to work.

The result of my visit to Guy's was that I ended up back in Harry Keen's office being asked, 'When can you start?' It turned out that the research fellow I was to take over from had already left for a new post in Newcastle and they were in a hurry to appoint someone to look after his patients and conduct the research projects which he had been involved in. I could not believe my luck, and wanted to start as soon as possible, which meant curtailing the three-month locum consultant job in Truro that I had taken on. I was very soon established and into the swing of things. Most of the patients for whom I was responsible would attend the Peter Bishop Metabolic Ward as outpatients, although sometimes they were required to stay overnight for a few days as an inpatient if a study necessitated this. I was responsible for conducting many of the monitoring tests, such as the isotope test for measuring a patient's kidney filtering function precisely.

There followed five years of some of the most exciting and rewarding times of my professional life. The unit at Guy's had been responsible for inventing the insulin pump, a novel way to continuously administer insulin under the skin to people with type 1 (insulin dependent) diabetes, and which proved to be successful in significantly ironing out the abnormal fluctuations in blood insulin – and therefore blood sugar – levels which treatment with conventional insulin injections was prone to. The near-normal control of a diabetic person's blood glucose levels that could now be obtained allowed us to examine more precisely the beneficial effects of improved blood glucose control in reducing both the development and progression of the serious complications which can occur in diabetes, especially blindness and kidney failure.

Whilst at Guy's Hospital, I was involved in the work to develop smaller insulin pumps, as well as having the responsibility of looking after many of the pump-treated patients and the studies they were recruited to. These studies came to be regarded as seminal, showing for the first time that the complications of diabetes could be prevented and arrested by significantly improved blood sugar control. The fact that I was given much of the responsibility for the care of these patients, including those with diabetic kidney disease, eye disease and foot disease, meant that the research projects I was involved in were largely clinically based and gave me a huge amount of further experience in the care and treatment of people with diabetes and its complications. I would also take part in the weekly diabetes and endocrinology clinics with the consultants and other research fellows.

The diabetes patients who had agreed to take part in one or other of our clinical research projects usually came to see me on a very frequent basis; this was part of the study protocol for measuring outcomes of treatment as the trials progressed. I therefore got to know the patients and their partners and families very well. They had my personal hospital 'bleep' number as well as my home telephone number and knew that I was happy for them to phone me at any time of the day or night should they require urgent advice. We also carried an out-of-hours 'air call' pager, which I shared with Dr John Pickup and Dr Gareth Williams, in order to provide around-the-clock advice 365 days a year for our pump patients. This close support was an important reason why our patients were able to achieve such excellent and prolonged improvement in the control of their diabetes;

a necessary objective if we were to prove the point that controlling diabetes well can prevent complications. It was a great honour to have been part of the Kroc study, the seminal study which we ran (along with other diabetes research centres in the US and Canada), which finally proved that this could be achieved. I acquired numerous papers in national and international journals during the course of this work, and wrote my doctorate MD thesis on the subject. The work also led to my being lucky enough to travel to many parts of the USA and the world to present papers and attend research meetings, while getting to know many of the leading international diabetes specialists in the process.

18

Listening Isn't Everything

I WAS TELEPHONED AT ABOUT SEVEN ONE EVENING, just as I had arrived back home, by Eileen, the wife of Raymond, who was one of my insulin-pump patients. She was concerned about her husband, who did not seem very well and whose blood sugar levels had been climbing uncharacteristically high during the course of the afternoon. 'Let me speak to Ray,' I said, reassuring her. Ray came to the phone and I talked to him for some time, asking about any possible symptoms he was experiencing. He denied any, only saying he 'did not feel himself' and that he was feeling a bit 'dry' because his blood sugar levels were up in the high teens. 'I am sure we can get these down, Ray, can't we? Hopefully that will help you feel better.' We agreed what the increase in his insulin infusion dose should be and I made sure he was testing his blood sugar levels very regularly with finger-prick tests, as well as checking that he was not developing any ketones in his urine. Thereafter, I telephoned Ray about every two hours. By about midnight, his blood sugars had settled to near normal and he told me he was feeling better. 'That's good,' I said, 'I'll call you in the morning but phone me at any time during the night if you or Eileen are worried. And bring yourself in to Guy's if you need to.'

I telephoned Eileen as soon as I woke the next morning at about six thirty. 'How is Ray?' I began.

'He's dead!' she replied, bursting into tears. She had apparently found her husband dead in bed when she had woken up herself. I was mortified to hear this and unable to explain what might have happened, but nevertheless did my best to console her over the phone. I went into work with a heavy heart, still unable to be sure what had happened, but also knowing that I had heard nothing on the telephone the evening before to predict this outcome. I had assumed from what he had told me that Ray was most likely suffering from a minor viral illness, which had been responsible for putting his blood sugar levels up.

It turned out that Raymond had died from a heart attack during the night, the cause of death demonstrated by a post mortem. At no time during the previous day had he complained of chest pains or other symptoms which might have suggested this possibility. The lack of symptoms, including chest pains, during a heart attack has been labelled a 'silent coronary'. This is said to occur more commonly in patients with diabetes. Its occurrence may have something to do with damage to the sensory nerves around the heart caused by diabetes, in turn removing the warning symptom that pain provides, although I believe this has never really been proven. I felt desperately sorry for Eileen, and told her so. I also knew, revisiting in my mind the advice and support I had given, that there was nothing to suggest that I should have acted differently from the way I did. The episode reinforced what I already knew, however: that 'telephone consultations' can be a trap for the unwary doctor. In a strange way, this was an example where being a listening doctor only (i.e. one speaking to a patient on the telephone) may have provided me with only partial information. If I had had the opportunity to look as well as to listen, in other words to observe my patient, I may have reached a different conclusion about his impending diagnosis. But I rather doubt it.

Whenever hospital managers were pressing hard for us consultants to undertake more telephone clinics, I remembered the case of Raymond. The managers were keen on this idea, of course, because it was seen as a cheap alternative to bringing patients up to hospital outpatient clinics, and therefore saved money and helped to reduce their waiting-time targets at the same time. It is a fact, in any case, that many of us consultants spend quite a deal of time telephoning patients to see how they are getting on – I used to do so – but we also know the importance of being able to see our patients and examine them if we are to make correct diagnoses and to avoid diagnostic errors. That's why the system was devised in the first place.

19

Stricken with Grief

THE DEATH OF A CHILD IS SOMETHING SO PROFOUND that probably only parents who have experienced the event can fully understand its enormity. The death of an adult child is appalling ('We never expected him/her to go before us'); the death of a young child is particularly tragic, a life stolen away prematurely ('He/she had his/her whole life ahead of him/her'). However, the death of an infant is often considered by those not involved to be little worse than a miscarriage or still birth, devastating though those events can often be for the bereaved parents.

My wife Jan was pregnant with our second child. The pregnancy had progressed uneventfully, with the normal growth of the foetus and a number of normal scans. Jan had for some reason been uneasy throughout this pregnancy, however, in a way that she had not been when carrying our first child, Jonathan. I had to go up to Edinburgh to deliver a paper to the British Diabetic Association Annual Conference. Since it was only about three weeks to go before she was due to give birth, Jan and Jonathan came with me so that we could all be together. The night before we were to return home, I was woken in our hotel room with a start by Jan who was screaming next to me in distress during a horrific nightmare. I had great trouble waking her and soothing her back to reality: 'Everything is all right, Darling. It was only a bad dream.'

When she was awake and calm enough to talk coherently, Jan described her dream to me. She was in the same room at Guy's Hospital where she had been when Jonathan was born. A lady had come into the room and told her that there was a problem with the baby and that they needed to get him out of her. She was put on a trolley and wheeled in to an operating room. Forceps were put inside her, and she felt the wrenching cold pain of this in the dream as her baby was pulled out. The next part of the dream found her back in the same room, but with no baby. She called for a nurse. The nurse came in to the room and she asked her about her baby. 'She wouldn't tell me, but the lady from before came in and told me that my baby had died of anasarca!' Jan cried to me. I reassured Jan that all was well and that such dreams are normal. Neither of us had heard of the word anasarca, further confirmation in my opinion that this was just a dream. I did my best to reassure Jan that her fears were no more than a mother's normal concerns for her unborn baby.

Oliver Adam Bending was born on 12 April 1984 at Guy's Hospital. Jan had had a normal pregnancy and she, Jonathan and I were very much looking forward to the birth of our second son. We knew he was a boy from scans done at around twenty weeks' gestation. We had also been reassured that all was well with the baby. In spite of Jan's forebodings, we continued to look forward, as parents do, to the birth of our child. We had chosen his name quite early on. Oliver was part of our lives throughout the pregnancy.

At his birth I held Jan's hand as we waited for our son to make his appearance, which he did with normal baby cries. Jan had some concerns about his colour, since he seemed a little blue, but he was of good birth weight (six pounds) and had normal Apgar birth scores (8 at one minute and 9 at five minutes). Oliver was born apparently healthy and most importantly a sentient being whose parents were full of joy at his birth. I can remember him lying in Jan's arms, dark haired and alert, at only a few hours old already appearing to be intelligent and aware of his surroundings and both his parents.

Oliver was born on a Thursday. On Friday, 13 April, my elderly father Roy visited his new grandson in Guy's Hospital and brought him a little teddy bear. I took a photo of Roy next to the cot in the hospital. Oliver seemed fine. On the Saturday, however, Jan became concerned by his lack of interest in feeding (she was breastfeeding) and mentioned this to the nurses. On the Sunday, Jan was sufficiently concerned to request an examination of Oliver by a paediatrician. She knew the medical and nursing staff thought she was being overanxious but he was her beloved baby. The lady paediatric registrar examined Oliver and said he was fine – 'a normal healthy baby' – and that he could be discharged and taken home with us that afternoon. I remember that drive home from Guy's to Lewisham. I drove very cautiously because of the precious load in Jan's arms.

Sunday night was terrible for Jan. Oliver wouldn't feed and started making grunting noises. I had to go to work on the Monday morning – there was no paternity leave in those days – but Jan assured me that the midwife would be calling and that she could cope. She also had Jonathan, then aged nineteen months, to look after. I left for work feeling very uneasy, but, in retrospect, I think wanting to reassure myself as well as my wife by carrying on as usual. By the time the midwife arrived later that morning Jan was desperate. She opened the door to her and said, 'My baby is dying.' Remember, she had been assured that he was fine a little more than twelve hours earlier.

I was sitting in the unit lunchtime meeting, chaired by Professor Harry Keen and with the whole of the Metabolic Unit team present, when the door flew open and Harry's secretary Jean came in looking anxious. 'There's an urgent phone call for Jeremy in the office,' Jean interrupted. I hurried out of the meeting to take the call.

'We have one very ill baby here, doctor,' the female GP at the other end of the phone told me. She was brusque and sounded rather cold. I was confused. What was the matter with Oliver? The lady GP actually sounded cross: had I done something wrong? 'I believe he is in congestive cardiac failure. I'm sending your wife and baby in to Guy's under a blue light.' Her diagnostic acumen could not be faulted, as it turned out. However, at the time, her telephone manner seemed inexplicably rough to me.

I made straight for the Emergency Department at Guy's. Within minutes Jan had arrived by ambulance in tears with baby Oliver in a shawl in her arms and little Jonathan in tow. The paediatric crash team whisked baby Oliver away and we were left sitting in a room by ourselves, in each other's arms. After a while the door opened and three very serious-looking senior doctors, including the professor of paediatric cardiac surgery, came in. Jan stood up with her arms held towards the men beseechingly but was told to sit down because 'the news was bad and could not be worse'. They explained that Oliver had a condition called hypoplastic left heart syndrome. The diagnosis had been confirmed by an advanced paediatric cardiac ultrasound scan, which had shown that the left side of his heart including the main left ventricle had not developed properly. This had caused no problems for his otherwise normal development while in the womb, when he was receiving his blood supply from his mother Jan. But his condition had deteriorated when the patent duct between the aorta and the left heart closed, as it does normally a few days after birth, and Oliver's unformed left heart had become unable to cope with providing blood to the rest of his body. We were told that the condition was inoperable and that they could keep him alive for a short time but that death was inevitable. Jan cried out 'where is my son?' and they told her that he was in an incubator in intensive care.

She ran out of the room, followed by myself with Jonathan, and we found our way to Paediatric Intensive Care. Oliver was lying in the incubator, very blue and struggling to breathe. He was struggling for life. Jan asked that he be taken out of the incubator to die in her arms. The staff were very sympathetic and we were put in a side room where Jan could nurse Oliver and spend the last precious moments with him. Jonathan was taken away by a friend for a while but brought back at 6.30 p.m. to say goodbye to his brother.

At around 7 p.m. we noticed Oliver was getting even more uncomfortable, so Jan asked for something she could give him to help calm him. Jan fed the medicine into his little mouth from a small syringe and baptised him with her own tears. She had been brought up a Catholic and been taught that this could be done in extremis. She had long since given up her faith but just felt that this was something she wanted to do. Oliver died at 7.15 p.m. on 16 April 1984. The shock and tragedy of all this is still difficult to report. I can still remember Jan sitting with her baby in her arms before having to hand him over to be certified as dead. We had to leave him at Guy's and took a bin liner home with us containing his few bits of clothing and Teddy. My brother Mike drove us home in his car and we spent the rest of the night in tears and phoning close family members to tell them the bad news.

The following days were dreadful. Jan's breasts ached with milk and a terrible emptiness took hold of us all. We would receive in the same batch of post cards of congratulation and letters of condolence. We had to decide what to do about Oliver's body. Easter was the following weekend and we were pushed to make a decision. Unable to bear the thought of our baby in the cold earth, we went for cremation. Oliver was cremated at Hither Green Crematorium in south London on 19 April 1984. We had a brief secular ceremony, during which I read the poem by W. B. Yeats, 'The Stolen Child':

> Away with us he's going,
> The solemn-eyed:
> He'll hear no more the lowing
> Of the calves on the warm hillside
> Or the kettle on the hob
> Sing peace into his breast,
> Or see the brown mice bob
> Round and round the oatmeal-chest.
> For he comes, the human child,
> To the waters and the wild
> With a faery, hand in hand,
> From a world more full of weeping than he
>   can understand.

Oliver's ashes were scattered on a rose bed there and no plaque or memorial was ever placed for him.

We received a copy of Oliver's autopsy report a few weeks after his death, confirming the fact that he had died from heart failure resulting from a congenital condition that had caused his left heart to not develop properly. We looked anasarca up in an ancient medical dictionary. It is the archaic word for congestive cardiac failure which results in collapse of the circulation and fluid filling the lungs. This was the cause of Oliver's death, secondary to hypoplastic left heart syndrome.

Being a doctor and a nurse did not help us to come to terms with our son's death and accept our tragedy. In some ways it may have made the tragedy more difficult to accept. Very shortly after Oliver's death, in July 1984, we were to read in the press about an eleven-day-old baby girl called Hollie Roffey who had received a heart transplant at the National Heart Hospital in London for the same condition, although she sadly died at four weeks old. I also came across articles in *The Lancet* reporting research into artificial hearts being used in the United States for this condition. We had been told truthfully at the time that nothing could be done to save Oliver, but could not but ask ourselves what might have happened had he been born a year or two later.

Others have written about their experience of their infant's death. The fact is that the grief caused is never less for the child being just a few days old – as in our Oliver's case – rather than a few years or a few decades old. It is also an experience that wounds permanently. For many couples, it can be the event that triggers the breakdown of their marriage. Sometimes, I had reason to fear that that might also be our fate. To this day, Jan never leaves Oliver out of her thoughts – not least on the anniversary of his birth and death, which are inevitably still black days for both of us – and Jan and I know she will never 'get over it' as she was immediately expected to do by some.

20

Listening to the Waves –
Beside the Seaside

AFTER THREE OR FOUR YEARS AT GUY'S WORKING AS
an honorary senior registrar and lecturer in medicine I
started to apply for consultant jobs of my own. The compe-
tition was fierce. At that time there were about twenty-nine
senior registrars applying for every consultant vacancy which
came up in the UK and, while it was not quite waiting for
dead men's shoes, there were a number of my peers who,
because of these unfavourable odds, made the decision to
change their career tack and left to join pharmaceutical
companies or emigrated down under etc. I always had two
CVs prepared and ready to go at any one time: one was
my 'academic' CV for the half a dozen professorial chairs
in medicine which I was interviewed for; the other was my
'DGH' CV, tailored to the equally numerous interviews
I was to receive for district general hospital consultant
posts. The somewhat depressing fact was that almost every
appointment went to the sitting candidate, and it was always
rather frustrating when, after much travelling and many

gruelling interviews, the person appointed was inevitably the man or woman already working as a senior registrar in the institution doing the interviewing. But I was determined to succeed and was not deterred.

I was aware, however, how very stressful the whole process was for my wife and the two young children we had at the time (our third son Adam having been born, also at Guy's Hospital, sixteen months after the death of Oliver). The fact was, we had no idea as a family when we were going to be able to settle down, and where that would be. We could have found ourselves in London, Newcastle, Manchester or Exeter, to name just a few of the places I had been invited to for a consultant post interview, not to mention anywhere else in the world!

The first interview that I went to unsure as to 'who has been earmarked for this one?' was for the consultant post at Eastbourne, on the South Coast of England, in 'Sussex by the Sea'. Although replacing a retired general physician, the job description was for their first ever consultant specialising in diabetes and endocrinology to set up a specialist service from scratch. My application had made it clear that my first aim was to build a diabetes specialist team and service, an important part of which would be raising the funds for and building and equipping a district diabetes centre out of which the team and the service could operate. I was interviewed with some nine other candidates. The interview seemed to go OK. Amongst the large panel of interviewers on the Consultant Appointments

Committee was one of my consultant colleagues from Guy's, Dr Giancarlo Viberti.

I was called in and offered the post. I still remember what a huge relief it was for both myself and my family after so many months and years struggling towards that day. We were to sell the house in Catford, south London, which we had only moved in to ten months before, and acquire a new home in Eastbourne barely four weeks before our only daughter Rachel was to be born. Although there was so much to do, and it was difficult to know where to start, I was clear in my mind that I had to establish a high-quality diabetes service before extending the reach of the department to take in all aspects of endocrinology, a project we were to complete some years later.

The one thing that I was very fortunate with was the fact that there already was the self-made nucleus of a diabetes team awaiting me. I had met up with Pari Sheppard before the interview. She was Iranian by birth, married to her husband Peter, who ran a ladies' hairdressing salon locally. Pari had been a sister on one of the medical wards at St Mary's Hospital in Eastbourne but, having a keen interest in diabetes, had essentially trained herself to become one of the first wave of diabetes specialist nurses in the UK. She was in the vanguard of nursing specialists. By the time I arrived in Eastbourne, her enthusiasm for her role had already led to her being elected to sit on the Diabetes Education Committee for the British Diabetic Association, as Diabetes UK was then called. Before I ever met Pari I knew how lucky

I was to be going to a position with a 'DSN' already in place, at a time when there were plenty of hospitals in the UK without any. ('What do we want one of them for?' I had heard people say. 'We do all that already.' One of the pioneering challenges for DSNs in our NHS was not only to raise the profile of diabetes care amongst people with diabetes, but also to educate their medical and nursing colleagues about the need for up-to-date diabetes treatment and care. And this remains the case today.) With Pari we had Lesley Houston, a recently qualified junior dietitian, who also had a keen interest in diabetes, and Alistair McInnes, a senior lecturer in the School of Podiatry down the road from the hospital in Eastbourne, who was equally interested in the serious problems that can arise with diabetes feet. The kernel of the team was in place.

Within four years of having taken up the post, I had managed to raise the money from charitable sources, and had built and equipped (with Pari's help) our 'state of the art' District Diabetes Centre. The centre featured as a template for diabetes-care delivery in a chapter in the *International Textbook for Diabetes*, which I wrote with my ex-boss Professor Harry Keen. The diabetes team and service was to go from strength to strength, followed a few years later by the addition of a comprehensive service in endocrinology, which we set up from scratch in a relatively small district general hospital.

21

Listening on the Wards

ON EVERY WARD ROUND MY RULE WAS TO STAND OUT-side the bay and talk about the patients we were about to see before proceeding to their beds. This would give the registrar or senior house officer a chance to present the case – the presenting history, the findings on examination of the patient and the results of blood tests, X-rays and other tests ('special investigations' as they are still rather quaintly called) – as well as a chance for us to peruse the vital information to be found in the patient's file of past medical history and treatments. I was insistent that we always included one of our nursing colleagues in both the ward round and these preliminary discussions. After all, the nurses are the ones that are caring for and observing the patients twenty-four hours a day; noticing essential signs or changes in a patient; and talking regularly to the family and carers, very often obtaining additional, sometimes vital, information about the patient. They were also expected to relay progress reports back to the relatives and to answer telephone calls from concerned family members. The best nurses would be enthusiastic to join in on these ward-round discussions – indeed they would run after me if I had called in to see a patient without them being present, wanting to know what had been said or planned for their patient. In other words, the caring nurse is an equally vital member of the team.

Sadly, in our present-day health service it has become increasingly common for doctors and nurses to go about their business separately. And the lack of a nurse to join the doctor's ward round seemed to have become almost the rule when entering a ward which was not one's base ward, which we were required to do on a daily basis. I would often be bluntly ignored when visiting a patient on one of the other wards in the hospital. It didn't bother me personally; I was never looking for an audience. But the idea that my patients and their needs might also be being given a lower priority concerned me greatly. If as doctors and nurses we lose the ability to communicate with each other, we do so at our own peril. And that of our patients, of course.

This system of discussing each patient prior to seeing them meant that I could be armed with the information I needed before I got to their bedside. This in turn allowed me to speak to the patient – and listen to them! – without standing at the end of the bed and going on about their case in the third person, as sometimes happened on the consultants' ward rounds I had experienced in my training days. It also gave me the advantage of being able to discuss confidential information outside the hearing of other patients in the same ward area, as well as the opportunity to teach the medical students and the other doctors in training as we went from case to case – something that I did routinely and constantly.

My registrar, Andy, was presenting a case to us: 'The girl in bed two is a twenty-two-year-old young lady who was admitted on take last night in fast atrial fibrillation and thyrotoxic heart failure.'

'Poor thing,' I said.

'In this case,' Andy went on, without judgement, 'I'm afraid to say the problem is self-inflicted.'

'How do you know?' I quizzed him.

'Her mother asked to talk to me in the office in private. She told me that Paula had had a problem with her body image since her early teens – she always felt that she was much too fat, although this was never the case – and that over the past year or so she had been consuming large amounts of thyroxine tablets in an attempt to lose weight. She had convinced herself that her weight was excessive.'

'How does the mother know this?' I asked.

'She recently found bottles of the tablets hidden under Paula's bed, most of them empty,' Andy replied. 'They had labels on them indicating that they had come from Florida. She had been buying them on the Internet.'

We arrived at the patient's bed, where I introduced myself. I could see that the poor girl was desperately ill. She was pitifully thin, with arms like sticks, and trembling uncontrollably, with a heart that was racing away at about 160 beats per minute in a completely irregular, erratic fashion. The result of this was that her heart could not cope – it had failed to keep up with its duties as a pump – and I could see that her neck veins were grossly engorged and she had oedema (swelling due to excess fluid) of both legs up to her groin, with fluid accumulating in her abdomen, which was distended and protuberant as a result. Her lungs were also full of fluid and she was gasping for breath. She was indeed in severe heart failure, but she had none of the other signs of classical Graves' disease (the most common cause of thyrotoxicosis or an over-active thyroid gland triggered by an autoimmune process – a failure in the immune system which 'turns the gauge on the thyroid up to overdrive'). Her thyroid gland was not enlarged, with no swoosh (bruit) of vascular over-activity heard as I listened with my stethoscope, and there was no evidence of exophthalmos, or 'poppy eyes'.

'What have you been doing to yourself, Paula?' I asked, as gently as I could.

'What do you mean?' she replied, looking at me defiantly.

'I understand you have been treating yourself with thyroxine tablets,' I said to her directly, not wanting to spend time beating about the bush.

'Only a few,' she had the courage at least to admit.

'Do you understand that this has made you very ill? It has put you into heart failure.' At this, Paula broke into floods of tears. Like most people who have become addicted to a drug, she was fully aware of the damage she had been doing to herself but had been quite unable to stop. She was desperate for help. 'Don't worry,' I consoled her, holding her hand. 'We will make you better, but you are going to have to stay in hospital for some weeks before you are well enough to go home. And when you do go home, we will give you all the help and support you need to not get back into the habit of swallowing this poison again.'

There are not too many causes of congestive heart failure presenting for the first time in a young woman of this age. But in endocrinological practice, thyroxine self-medication has unfortunately ceased to be a rare occurrence. Over the last few decades I had come across the unregulated pre-scribing of thyroxine by unscrupulous private practitioners, usually to women desperate to lose weight; particularly by one gentleman in the borough of Croydon, south London, who was eventually struck off the medical register by the General Medical Council for this practice. More recently, the use of medical drugs for self-abuse – including that of simple thyroxine, which is absolutely essential for the health of people whose thyroid glands have become underactive – has become much more common and been made increas-ingly possible by their unregulated sale on the Internet. The poor girl had probably paid out hundreds of pounds over the previous year in her desperate attempt to acquire a drug which, on prescription, actually only costs pennies, but which in her case had brought her to the threshold of death.

22

Listening in the Outpatient Clinic

IT IS WELL KNOWN THAT PATIENTS ATTENDING A HOS-pital outpatients' clinic for a consultation take away, on average, only a small percentage of what has been discussed and said to them. Perhaps only twenty-five per cent, if you are lucky. Which means, of course, that some seventy-five per cent of what has been discussed has either not been understood or retained – for whatever reason – by the time the patient has left the consulting room. This is not a criticism of patients – I know I've been one of them! – but the fact that this is so should always be remembered. In my experience the reasons for this are many. For a start, patients are, by definition, usually ill people. This means they may not have the energy, hearing, intelligence, ability – the list is infinite – to understand and absorb what is being said to them. Although they might not admit it, almost all the patients I saw were frightened, in one way or another.

One of the most effective ways of ensuring that a patient has understood what has been said to them, and to reinforce the message, is to have a nurse skilled in communication in the room at the time of the consultation. The nurse will sit down with the patient after he/she has left the room and take the time to enquire as to whether the person has understood what has been said and to reinforce the messages that have been given. This is essential when the consultation has been involved in breaking bad news – giving a diagnosis of life-threatening disease or curtailed life-expectancy – but is just as important in reinforcing more day-to-day – but equally important to the patient – health advice.

Over the years, I have come to appreciate that the effectiveness of the nurse taking on this role has nothing to do with their seniority, qualifications or their status in the nursing hierarchy. Nurses, like doctors, are able to communicate well, or they are not. In my later years, I came to value and appreciate the assistance of a health care assistant who was excellent in this role of supporting patients and their families. Julie was a woman of maturity (in the nicest sense of the word) who instinctively knew how to run my clinic and, most importantly, put patients at their ease (she also put me at my ease, which was equally important!). The fact that she was affectionately known as 'Matron' by her dozens of nursing colleagues – including the senior state-qualified ones – tells its own story. She might have been paid a pittance for her work, but she was worth her weight in gold, as far as I and my patients were concerned.

The fact that patients' retention of knowledge is so incomplete also means that, in the care of people with chronic (meaning long-standing or life-long) disease, such as diabetes and hypertension (high blood pressure), it is essential that advice given is repeated and reinforced at every visit – whether this be by the doctor, specialist nurse, dietitian, podiatrist or whichever member of the team the patient visits at any given consultation. It is also vital that any advice given is up to date, consistent and given in a way that is *understandable* to the patient concerned. There is nothing more dispiriting for a patient than to be given some advice by, say, an experienced diabetes specialist nurse which is then disagreed with by, say, a practice nurse in his or her surgery. In order to help make any health advice message understood, it goes without saying that advice should be given in different ways at the same time. What I mean by this is that verbal advice should be supplemented by written advice (in plain, easy-to-read English!) and in other ways such as videos played in the waiting room and (particularly effective) small-group patient discussions. There is nothing quite as therapeutic for someone with diabetes as finding out that there are so many other people 'out there' with the same problems and that the advice and treatment approach they have received is the same as their own.

As I walked along the corridor, either to or from my outpatient clinic, I would frequently find myself smiling at a conversation overheard between a patient and their relative who were leaving one of the other clinics still in progress – a wife quizzing her husband, for instance: 'Well, what did he say about it?' or something similar, was the reasonable question she would be asking and very often, as

I turned the corner, I would hear the reply, 'I'm not really sure.' Or I might even just catch out of the corner of my eye a silent shrug in reply. It is for this reason that when seeing a patient, especially for the first time, I always tried whenever possible to get a spouse, partner, parent, child or carer to accompany them.

23

'Now Listen to Me!' –
The 'Expert' Patient

ALL DOCTORS UNDERSTAND THE NEED FOR PATIENTS to be involved in their own illness and its treatment if they are going to recover from it, or at least control it. That's just another way of saying that the healing process is not just about medicine and drugs. The recovery from illness very much involves the 'will' or the 'spirit' – call it what you wish. As doctors, we can all remember patients who were expected to die but 'refused' to do so and eventually recovered from the fatal prognosis which they had been given in good faith. Conversely, I can remember many of my patients who shouldn't have died – they did not appear to have a terminal illness – but nevertheless proceeded to do so. In the second category belong people who had lost their life-long partner (recently-widowed men especially) who then died unexpectedly not a long time after. This really is not so uncommon. Some might describe it as dying from a broken heart. Most of my cardiology colleagues would very likely dismiss this possibility as hogwash (particularly one or two of the 'Type A' interventionist heart doctors I know – their patients seem never to die, or if they do, they would not admit to it!) but my experience speaks to the contrary.

Awareness of the importance of the human spirit in fighting disease is therefore an essential part of being a good doctor, as far as I am concerned. Some would call it having a holistic approach to medicine. Many people seem to believe that the doctors of today in our modern health service somehow do not have this approach; a point of view often fostered by non-registered 'alternative' practitioners, I have to say. But these 'alternative' practitioners may be surprised to know that they do not have a monopoly on treating ill people holistically. I believe this has always been part of basic good medical practice.

The importance of recruiting ill people to learn about their own illness and to help themselves in its treatment is not new, therefore. This concept was highlighted by a campaign in the early part of this century, launched in an attempt to foster an understanding of it in all patients. And it is a particularly important goal when caring for people with chronic life-long conditions such as diabetes. There is a lot of talk about the need for 'lifestyle' changes with diabetes as well as other conditions. ('Lifestyle' is a word which, I have to say, is often used with a whiff of paternalism: 'Don't do as I do. Do as I say!') And it is absolutely true that, if patients with the condition are able to make changes in order to adopt a healthy diet, lose some weight, take some exercise and so on, all this adds a lot to any other treatment they might require. Studies prove that making these changes can help control diabetes significantly and prolong both quality and length of life. As I used to say to my patients, 'You can't *prescribe* a low HbA1c!' (The HbA1c is a blood test which tells us about the medium-term average blood glucose level of a person with diabetes. A low result is consistent with blood sugars being well under control. And vice versa. 'But it is not a beauty contest!' I was also fond of saying.) In other words, all the blood sugar lowering drugs in the world, and indeed insulin injections, will not control a patient's diabetes if the person does not wish this to happen by observing the need for diet and exercise as well.

Having said all this, there did seem to be something just a little patronising about the Department of Health sponsored campaign that championed patient involvement in their own illness or disease. Entitled 'The Expert Patient', it suggested that this was a novel idea which had not existed before and which would revolutionise medical practice and facilitate better health outcomes for all. The Department of Health is very good at setting targets which satisfy politicians' wishes but which tend to measure the process of medical care rather than the outcome. Targets in medicine are all well and good, but all doctors have to accept that they cannot cure 'all of the people all of the time' and have to respect the right of any patient to reject their advice and 'live for today'. In my experience this is no less the case when respecting the wishes of the older patients, for whom quality of life becomes increasingly more important than quantity as the evening of life draws in.

On the other side of the coin, doctors in both general practice and hospital medicine will frequently be faced with a patient who comes into the consulting room already convinced that they know what is wrong with them and what treatment they require. And some of these will *demand* that treatment if they don't get it! In this day and age many patients will have spent a considerable amount of time researching their illness, or at least their symptoms, on the Internet before visiting a doctor, and especially before a visit to a specialist. Don't get me wrong, in general I believe this is a good thing, although knowledge gained in this way, without an explanation about what it all means and adequate support, can also frighten people and even induce hypochondriasis in some. I would often have to gently point out to a patient that, coming as it did from the Internet, the information they had been given was not necessarily correct. Or, if it was, that it might not be applicable to them personally. 'There are plenty of quacks on the web,' I would say. 'Beware especially if the information comes from across the water and is accompanied by a request for your credit card details with a view to shipping with speed to you the magic remedy for your ailment. The seller in this case is no better than the guy who used to stand on the back of a wagon in the American Far West offering up a bottle of green water as the elixir of life!' I used to quip.

★

Daphne marched in to my consulting room. 'Are you the consultant?' she demanded as I introduced myself to her.

'I am,' I said.

'And you are a thyroid specialist?' her interrogation continued.

'I am, also,' I said, as politely as possible.

'Good!' Daphne exclaimed, letting air out of her mouth like a deflating balloon as she collapsed into the chair next to me. 'You're just the man I need!'

'Tell me what the problem is,' I prompted her, raising my eyebrows just a fraction as I did so.

'I've been ill for years and nobody will listen to me,' Daphne complained.

'Can you be more specific?' I asked.

'Well,' she said, 'I'm tired all the time – exhausted in fact! I feel cold, depressed and have put on a huge amount of weight. Added to which my husband complains that I don't love him anymore, if you know what I mean. And that's just for starters.' My pen hovered over the page. 'I know my thyroid gland is underactive, I've read about it on the Internet, but my GP has refused to treat me. I don't have confidence that he knows anything about the thyroid gland and I had to insist that he refer me to a thyroid specialist. It's taken over six months to get to see you!'

I nodded at Daphne understandingly as I pushed on with taking my usual complete history of the patient's presenting complaints: her past medical history; her family history, particularly relating to instances of thyroid or any other 'autoimmune endocrine diseases' (there were none); her drug and allergy history; as well as a checklist of her bodily systems; all of which filled more than two sides of A4 in this case. 'Come on, then,' I said, having completed my history taking, 'let's have a look at you.' Daphne undressed and got on the couch with Matron Julie's help. What I found when I examined the lady was that she was indeed significantly overweight – the clinic scales had told me that already – but that her thyroid was normal, as was the rest of her, and I certainly could find no evidence of a thyroid disorder.

I returned to my desk and sat there completing my notes as I gave Daphne time to dress herself again. She threw the curtains back from around the couch and came to sit down beside me again. 'Well?' she demanded.

I faced her question head on: 'I am pleased to tell you Daphne that I am unable to find anything to suggest that you have a disease of your thyroid gland.'

'That can't be right!' Daphne exploded. 'I've read a lot about it and know that the symptoms I have are exactly the same as the symptoms of an underactive thyroid. I need treatment with thyroxine, but my GP refuses to prescribe it for me.'

'Unfortunately,' I did my best to explain, 'the symptoms you have may occur for many different reasons. I can find no evidence from your history and examining you that thyroxine treatment is necessary or indeed appropriate. And your repeatedly normal thyroid blood tests also reassure us that this is correct.' Daphne was not looking satisfied. 'Besides,'

I went on, 'the British Thyroid Association, of which I am a member (I was not pulling rank here, you understand, just trying to add whatever I could to reassure her!) reminds us that prescribing thyroxine can even be harmful for people who do not need it (poor Paula, for one). That is why it is listed in the *British National Formulary* as a prescription-only drug.'

(When I see a patient who clearly does have an under-active thyroid but who is wary about the need for swal-lowing thyroxine tablets every day for the rest of their life, I often reassure them that, 'thyroxine is not really a drug. It is a synthetically manufactured version of the hormone which your thyroid gland was producing but has stopped producing. Think about it as thyroid hor-mone replacement therapy – THRT. Besides, thyroxine in normal physiological amounts does not have any side effects. We can't say that about any other drug known to medicine!' Two-faced of me? Not really. I just try to give the best advice and support to each patient, as required in each individual case.)

Daphne was definitely not satisfied. In fact, I could see her face reddening before my eyes as her anger rose. 'I'm sorry doctor, but you've got it wrong in my case!' she said, by now indicating that she was not feeling at all well-disposed towards me.

'What I am going to do,' I told her, 'is send a full report of my findings to your GP. I will send a copy of this letter to you as well. When you have had time to read it and consider what I have said, you might find it helpful to make an appointment with your GP to discuss the situation further.'

'Hummph,' Daphne snorted, clearly angry and disgruntled.

'I wish you well,' I said as Julie showed her back out to the waiting room.

As a younger consultant I might have spent a considerable amount of time trying to persuade Daphne, at the cost of keeping numbers of other ill patients outside waiting unfairly. But, by this time, it was already clear that Daphne was not prepared to be persuaded that her self-diagnosis and need for treatment was wrong. Sometimes, if a patient in front of me was wavering about whether they believed what I was saying, I would say something like 'if you take your car to the garage to be mended, you do have to trust the mechanic before he looks under your bonnet' or 'I promise you that the advice I have given you is exactly the same as that which I would give if you were a member of my own family' – both tactics designed to try and persuade a patient that I did mean well. If any of my patients asked for a second opinion, I was always very happy to agree. But, on this occasion, I didn't offer one, because I did not think that that would help Daphne come to terms with her problem. You may have noticed, by the way, that I did not give her an explanation as to what I thought her legion of complaints were due to. Having satisfied myself that I could find no clear evidence of serious disease which might need treatment, I had stuck to the particular thyroid issue, and batted the rest of it back to her GP with whom responsibility for such concerns lay. The straightforward consultations with the grateful patients are the easy ones. The difficult consultations with the ungrateful patients are the challenging ones. But as physicians we are here to give our best advice, not always to be liked.

It may have been that, practising as I was amongst a largely middle class and educated population on the South Coast of England, the level of knowledge of my patients, and consequently their expectations, was higher than in many other parts of the United Kingdom. My friend Roger Wolstenholme, with whom I had trained, spent his consultant life as a chest physician in the town of Wigan, in the North West of England. He told me how it was not unusual for him to have a consultation with a retired miner who would sit in front of him in the clinic still wearing his cloth cap. 'I'm very sorry, Fred,' he would say to the patient, pointing to a shadow on the man's chest X-ray on the screen in front of them. 'You've got a tumour in the lung. It's cancer. I'm afraid it's inoperable and going to kill you.'

'Don't worry, doctor. Thank you for letting me know. You've done your best,' the man would reply, accepting the situation philosophically, while Roger knew that in fact all he had really done was to see the patient at an initial consultation, arrange for a chest X-ray and show him the result at a follow-up. The stoicism and acceptance of death was admirable, and the level of neurosis about imagined disease in the north of the country apparently much lower than in the south.

It was certainly the case that expectations for health and greater longevity in my patients, and especially in their relatives, rose exponentially during the more than a quarter of a century in which I practised as a consultant physician. That in itself, of course, is no bad thing. A less desirable feature of this is the increasing difficulty society has – we all have – in accepting death, which is, after all, inevitable. It is quite alarming that the children and other family members of our elderly population are often unable to accept the fact that their ninety-three-year-old granny is about to die.

I did not undertake much private practice, particularly at the start of my consultant life when I was putting all my energy into establishing my NHS service in diabetes and endocrinology – building up from scratch a service, a team and a state-of-the-art District Diabetes Centre for them to operate out of. Besides, I did not consider that people with chronic conditions such as diabetes should have to pay to receive treatment. I would say to those patients with diabetes who did ask to come and see me privately, 'I understand that you wanted to see me quickly and personally. But if you come to our diabetes centre at the hospital under the NHS you will meet our whole team of excellent diabetes specialist nurses, dietitians and podiatrists. What do you think about that?'

The fact of the matter was, in any case, that their insurance company would usually make the decision for them.

Most health care insurers are happy to take your money by direct debit every month for many years, and will cover you if you need a one-off operation in a private hospital for something finite. However, when it comes to informing them that you have developed a long-term chronic disease like diabetes, they usually don't want to know and exclude the condition from your private health cover with them.

One thing private practice did provide, particularly in my early days as a consultant, however, was an opportunity to learn to deal with those patients who had the very highest expectations. To say that they often 'wanted to be seen yesterday and treated the day before' was not too much of an exaggeration. But it did teach me to manage people's expectations, which was useful also in the running of my mainly NHS practice.

24

Type Two – You Too?

DIABETES IS AN ANCIENT DISEASE. THE FIRST RECORDED mention of the condition was by Aretaeus of Cappadocia in the first century A.D. He named the affliction 'the pissing evil' in recognition of the frequent urination which is a consequence of high blood sugar levels driving large volumes of urine through the kidneys. Diabetes mellitus, to give it its full name, is derived from the Greek word *diabetes* (that is, a siphon; referring to this increased urination) and the Latin word *mellitus* (that is, 'honeyed', or 'sweet'; referring to the sweetness of the urine which spills out, carrying some of the high glucose levels from the blood with it). It is perhaps the only disease in the English language which mixes a Greek word with a Latin word.

Jeffrey was a fifty-two-year-old school teacher. He was sitting in my consulting room in the Diabetes Centre, having been referred by his GP with newly diagnosed type 2 diabetes. This had come to light recently during the routine screening made when he had signed on with the practice, having moved to the area from south London to teach at a new school in Eastbourne. I could see that he was still shocked by the news. He told me he had not been aware of any symptoms, although on questioning he did admit to having felt more tired than usual – which he'd assumed was related to his recent move – and that he had been getting up more than once a night to pee over the past few months, which was unusual for him.

'I can't believe this has happened to me, Dr Bending. I've not had a day off sick in my life, and I don't know of anyone in my family who has had diabetes,' he said. I explained to him gently that, although diabetes does occur more frequently in some families, it is not always the case that diabetes patients have a family history of the condition. I started to describe in simple terms the nature of the con-dition, stressing particularly the fact that, now that it had developed, we could help him understand how he could best control the disorder. He was an intelligent man who was already aware that no cure existed as of yet and that the condition usually does progress over the years, requir-ing increasing levels of treatment and sometimes insulin injections in time. I did not disabuse him of these facts, but did my best to stress the importance of simple measures, such as concentrating on improving his diet, regular exercise and aiming for some weight loss, which he clearly needed.

When I got Jeffrey on the couch to examine him, I found that he had markedly elevated blood pressure (confirming his practice nurse's findings – I also knew that he had been found to have very high blood-cholesterol levels). He'd had his visual acuity checked on a reading chart on arrival at the Diabetes Centre by the checking-in nurse, who had also instilled eye drops into his eyes. His pupils were by now well dilated, and using my ophthalmoscope to examine his retinae – the photographic plates at the back of the eyes – I found that he had already developed quite advanced retinopathy: there was damage to the small blood vessels and retinal tissues. Moving down to examine his feet, I found he had partially lost his sense of feeling, indicating that the peripheral sensory nerves were affected by the diabetic process.

Putting all these findings together, I concluded that Jeffrey had had diabetes for some years at least, even though he had not been aware of the fact, during which the complications of the disease had already had time to develop. This is not uncommon: the symptoms of the disease – including non-specific tiredness and increasing frequency of urination, as in Jeffrey's case – are insidious, coming on very slowly and often not marked enough to prompt the person to take themself down to see their doctor. Many people have the disease for a decade or more before it is actually diagnosed. This fact underlines a challenge facing the health system: if the disease is to be picked up and treated early, it is necessary to screen asymptomatic people who don't know they already have the condition, especially those with risk factors for developing the condition such as a strong family history, racial factors, obesity, and so on. And once diagnosed, it is important to screen the person for other issues, on the assumption that established complications may very well already be present.

I sat Jeffrey back down next to me and discussed the situation with him. If when he arrived he had appeared shocked by the recent news of his initial diagnosis, he was now having to deal with the fact that he had diabetes, hypertension and high-cholesterol levels – the 'triple whammy', which it is not unusual to find in newly diagnosed type 2 diabetes patients. He was going to have to start taking blood pressure- and cholesterol-lowering tablets for the rest of his life, not to mention the increasing number of drugs to control his diabetes over the coming years. The fact that this news is hard to take – perhaps especially for a man, and one who had never been ill in his life before – goes without saying. When I had finished breaking the news to him as gently as I could, and accentuating what we could do to help and – equally important – what he could do to help himself, I led him down the corridor to meet up with Janet, our diabetes specialist dietitian, and Sally, one of our diabetes specialist nurses. He was offered intensive and ongoing help for the following months and advice about how he could learn about, and manage, his own condition. In addition, he was invited to our type 2 diabetes group training sessions, where he would meet other people like himself.

Type 2 (non-insulin dependent) diabetes accounts for something like ninety per cent of the disease in the UK. And the condition's prevalence is increasing at an alarming rate, reaching epidemic proportions. Although previously labelled 'maturity onset' diabetes – to distinguish it from the largely 'juvenile onset' of type 1 (insulin dependent) diabetes – over the past few decades there has been an explosion of type 2 diabetes, associated with rising obesity levels and sedentary lifestyles, in people of all ages, including in children and young people: 'maturity onset diabetes of youth', or MODY as it is sometimes called. And the indication is that this epidemic is set to worsen significantly over the next few decades.

While unified by the same deficiency – the loss of the body's ability to regulate the metabolism of glucose and other body chemicals normally – the two conditions are essentially quite different beasts. Type 1 diabetes (T1DM) is the result of the body's malfunctioning immune system destroying the pancreatic beta cells responsible for the production of insulin. Type 2 diabetes (T2DM) arises out of a resistance to the action of the hormone insulin on the body's tissues – 'insulin resistance' – and is particularly associated with obesity, especially that of around the abdomen. Indeed, early on in the course of T2DM blood-insulin levels are often found to be higher than normal as the pancreas pours out excess levels of insulin in an attempt to overcome this resistance, but eventually the pancreas starts to become exhausted by this increased output and begins to fail. Either way, the loss of the production of insulin or the resistance of the body's tissues to its action means that blood glucose levels rise out of control and the person becomes diabetic.

For decades type 2 diabetes was considered by many as a kind of 'mild' diabetes. Unfortunately, this was a major error of understanding about the condition, which omitted the fact that not only are people with type 2 diabetes also at risk of developing small blood vessel damage, leading to retinopathy (and loss of sight), nephropathy (and kidney failure), neuropathy (loss of nerve function) and ischaemia (loss of blood supply) – the last two both leading to foot infections, gangrene and risk of amputation of the lower limb – but they are also more likely to develop disease of the large blood vessels, leading to cardiovascular disease (angina and heart attacks) and cerebrovascular disease (strokes), all of which occur more commonly in people with T2DM and at a relatively earlier age. This common misconception, resulting entirely from a lack of knowledge, led to type 2 diabetes being often quite frankly ignored in the community. At the time I was appointed a consultant physician specialising in diabetes – the first such specialist to be appointed in Eastbourne – people in the UK with type 2 diabetes were clearly treated as the poor cousins of diabetes care: in effect, screening for the disease and structured quality care for those who had it – including the screening for and prevention of the complications listed above – was virtually non-existent. People with T2DM were being largely overlooked.

For these reasons, over the past few decades diabetes specialists and diabetes specialist nurses have had to face the challenge of educating colleagues, both in general practice and hospital medicine, about the importance of type 2 diabetes. From the outset, I and my DSN colleagues made it clear that we were happy to see people with both type 1 and 2 diabetes; that we did not discriminate between patients based on their disease label or method of treatment. I would not infrequently be asked by incredulous GP colleagues, 'Do you *really* want to see all those people with mild diabetes?!' I had to repeatedly explain that diabetes is a condition which can maim and kill, whatever type it is and whatever treatment may be being given at any point. We knew we could not see them all, but we maintained our willingness to keep our doors open for people with T2DM as much as T1DM – especially those whose diabetes was proving difficult to control, or who were developing the complications of the disease. This aspect was important in raising the profile of what was, after all, the type of diabetes that affected the majority of those with the condition.

Just like other diabetes specialist teams nationally, we knew there was no way that we could see the huge and growing army of people with T2DM in our area without help and that we had to encourage doctors and nurses to develop structured quality care for the condition in general practice if the burden of the disease was to be tackled and its treatment improved. An important aspect of improving the standard of care for people with type 2 diabetes is to educate those with the condition about what treatment they should expect, wherever their diabetes is being cared for. The national organisation Diabetes UK tries to disseminate this information to all people with diabetes. One vehicle we established locally to support this was group training sessions for people with T2DM, which not only helped people with diabetes manage their own condition, but also raised the awareness in all people with T2DM that they have a right to high-quality structured care and what this should mean.

25

'Listening Is All I've Got'

MARILYN WAS A THIRTY-TWO-YEAR-OLD WOMAN WHO had suffered from type 1 (insulin dependent) diabetes for twenty years. I had met her on and off over those years, but only very infrequently. The reason for this was that Marilyn almost never turned up for the clinic appointments which had been offered to her, or to see one of our excellent DSNs in the Diabetes Centre. As far as I knew, she did not bother to attend her general practice either.

We had spent a lot of time in the early years trying to keep in contact with her. The DSNs had encouraged her, telephoned her (when she had a phone that was working) and even called round to visit her in her very squalid basement flat, where she lived on her own or with her succession of short-term partners. The few times we did get to see her were when she had been admitted as an emergency to the Intensive Care Unit in the hospital with life-threatening diabetic ketoacidosis (DKA), her diabetes dangerously out of control with high blood sugars and ketoacids in her blood, or after she has been found collapsed and unconscious at home as a result of a severe hypoglycaemic (low blood sugar) coma. She would require a number of days' treatment for an episode of DKA, comprising intensive treatment with saline and electrolytes, insulin being infused into her veins and the continued monitoring of her cardiac rhythm and vital signs, as well as the frequent measurement of her blood glucose and chemistry. On more than one occasion she had signed herself out of the hospital after a life-threatening episode while still not well enough to go home and with her diabetes still not under anything like adequate control – self-discharging 'against medical advice'. She was followed-up on each occasion with supportive phone calls from the DSNs and given clinic appointments, all of which she again failed to attend. At this point, all we could do was to inform her GP of her failures to attend and stress that we would be happy to see her again at any time, if she could be persuaded to come.

In addition to not availing herself of basic diabetes care, Marilyn would also not bother to access all the other services which were hers by right as somebody with diabetes, such as annual screening for the development of eye, kidney and foot complications. When I had the opportunity to discuss her case from time to time at our team meetings, medical students and junior doctors were often quite astounded to hear that someone with such a serious disease, but with complications that were preventable, should not bother to look after themselves. 'Why doesn't she come?' they would ask.

'I haven't been able to find out the reason from her,' I would reply. The common reasons for a patient failing to attend are their fear of their own disease, fear of hospitals, fear of doctors, apathy and depression or the fact that they will lose pay if they take time off work. Some people, with chronic diseases particularly, take a conscious decision to 'live life for today', whatever tomorrow might bring. It is a decision which I have to respect, even if I disagree with it – respect that is, after I am sure that I have been clear enough in explaining to the patient, in a way that they understand, that all of the complications of their disease are now essentially preventable if they can find the time to follow the advice.

'But why can't you *insist* that they attend, Dr Bending?!' a medical student might ask me.

'You will learn when you are qualified that you cannot cure all of the people all of the time. As a doctor we are not gods and try our very best not to be, even though we do have to make life and death decisions on a daily basis in the interests of our patients. But it is a patient's choice to accept our advice and also to reject it, if that is what they decide. I cannot persuade anyone to swallow a simple aspirin if they do not wish to do so! It is, after all, a free society, and we have to accept patient choice, even if, as in cases like this, we might do so with a heavy heart.'

Late one Friday afternoon, Marilyn walked in to the Diabetes Centre asking to see one of the DSNs. Pari came in to see me. 'She's pregnant,' she told me 'and unfortunately well into the second trimester (second third) of her pregnancy. Her blood glucose is 23.5 mmol/l (very high) and she has got two-plus ketones in her urine, which is probably not unusual for Marilyn.'

(The importance of this information which Pari was giving me was that there was a high risk of complications to both the mother and the unborn baby; these are usually avoided if the woman is given every help available to control her diabetes before pregnancy even occurs. Organogenesis – the development of major body organs – occurs at an early stage of pregnancy: the foetal heart, for instance, is formed about five weeks into the pregnancy, at a time when many women may only just be aware that they have missed a period. For this reason, we stress to all women of child-bearing age the importance of pre-pregnancy counselling and intensive diabetes care.)

'Well at least she's shown up,' I replied. 'Let's do our best to persuade her to keep in contact.'

'I tried to persuade her that she should be admitted for a few days' monitoring, to see if we could help get her diabetes under better control, but she refused,' Pari said. 'I've given her an appointment to come back to see me on Monday morning, however, and I think I've at last persuaded her to do some blood glucose self-monitoring (with finger-prick testing) over the weekend.'

Late on Monday morning Pari came in to see me in my office, just as I had returned from finishing my morning ward round. 'Marilyn has shown up,' she said.

'That's wonderful news!' I replied.

'Not so wonderful, I'm afraid,' Pari continued. 'She's done no blood glucose testing over the weekend and the reason she has given me is that she says she cannot see the numbers on the meter I gave her.' I hurried round with Pari to her room next door. Marilyn was sitting there looking blankly into the middle distance. As I examined her vision, I was alarmed to find that she could not even count the number of fingers I had held up in front of her face. When I tried to examine her retinas with my ophthalmoscope, my view was occluded by a sea of blood. She had suffered bilateral vitreous haemorrhages – bleeding from small pathological vessels at the back of both eyes, which had developed as a result of her poor long-term diabetes control denying the retinal tissues a normal oxygen and nutrient supply.

I rushed Marilyn from the Diabetes Centre straight over the car park to the main hospital, holding her by the hand on the way across. She stumbled once or twice on the way, when I failed to warn her in time about a curb to be negotiated, and I had to steady her from falling, in the process confirming my depressing assessment that she had indeed lost her sight. I took her in to see one of my consultant ophthalmology colleagues, who verified my diagnosis, substantiating my worst fears. From then on Marilyn's vision was in his hands. He did everything that he possibly could in an attempt to regain some sight for her – vitrectomy surgery (removing the blood clots from the supporting fluid in the eyeballs) followed by laser treatment – while I and my DSNs did our very best to help her with her diabetes control. The long story short, however, was that the eye specialist was unable to regain any meaningful sight for Marilyn. His stark words to me were that she had 'no visual potential'. Marilyn was registered blind. When I returned to the Diabetes Centre after the final eye clinic assessment, I broke the news to the rest of the diabetes team. 'If *only* she had at least attended the annual retinal screening appointments! Her sight loss could have been prevented with laser treatment. It's so sad.'

I received a call from the hospital at 11 p.m. on a Saturday night. Marilyn had been admitted in premature labour, at only about thirty-four weeks' gestation (seven and a half months into her pregnancy). We put her on an insulin and glucose infusion and her diabetes was kept nice and stable throughout labour and delivery. Her baby had to be cared for in the special care baby unit for twenty-four hours after its birth because she was so premature and her blood sugar levels tended to be on the low side, as is often the case. The newborn's pancreas has to recalibrate itself to put out less insulin, having been used to coping with abnormally high sugar levels from its mum over its months in the womb. But the babe's blood sugars soon settled down very quickly to normal. She at least did not have diabetes at birth.

I went to visit Marilyn in the Obstetric Unit after my ward round on the Monday morning. She was sitting cuddling little Zoe, who was making gurgling noises. 'She sounds so happy!' Marilyn said to me, beaming.

'She looks just like her mum,' I said, lightheartedly. Marilyn turned her head vaguely in my direction.

'I wish I could see her,' she said to me sadly. 'Listening is all I've got.' I turned away from Marilyn with tears in my eyes. It was a reflex action, and I knew very well that Marilyn could not have seen my tears.

As it turned out, all was not well with baby Zoe. I learned later that, not only had she been found to have a hole in her heart, which I believe was operated on successfully, but the little girl also had cerebral palsy as a result of her diabetes and very premature birth. I also learned that the child later had to go into full-time care because Marilyn was unable to cope with looking after her. The baby died within a year or two of her birth. The beast that is diabetes can get to you even before you are born, I thought to myself when I heard this news.

26

Listening Together

STAN WAS A NICE MAN IN HIS SEVENTIES. HE HAD worked as a farmhand and gamekeeper for much of his life but in the last few decades had also built up a very successful business, which carried his name, selling Land Rover vehicles of all types, both new and second hand. He always came to the clinic with his supportive wife Audrey. 'How do you feel about what we have just told you?' I asked him. We had been discussing the options relating to kidney dialysis and transplantation. Stan had started to develop a leak of protein in his urine, one of the hallmarks of diabetic kidney disease, about twenty years before and his kidney function had been declining slowly but steadily over the last few years. He still had no significant symptoms, apart from the fact that he found himself becoming very easily tired, which he had supposed was normal for his age.

'Don't worry about making any decisions now,' my colleague Chris said to him. 'When you get a bit nearer the time, I will arrange for you to come over for a visit to our Kidney Dialysis Unit and meet up with one of our dialysis nurses who will show you how it all works.' Stan already knew that he was unlikely to be put on the list for a kidney transplant from elsewhere, because of his age and other health problems, but he had a very caring daughter who was keen to offer her father one of hers. The alternative was for him to undergo kidney dialysis in the hospital three times a week, which he might in any case require before his transplant or after it if the transplant did not go well.

We were sitting in the Joint Diabetes Renal Clinic, myself, Stan and his wife, together with my colleague Dr Chris Kingswood, the senior kidney specialist (nephrologist) from Brighton, who came over to Eastbourne six times a year for the purpose of the joint clinic. As diabetologists, we were used to doing joint clinics together with other specialties. We ran a multidisciplinary footcare clinic which involved a diabetologist, a DSN, a specialist diabetes podiatrist and visits from our vascular surgeon colleague when he was not operating. The Joint Diabetes Antenatal Clinic was another important service, also originally established by myself but by then run by my consultant diabetologist colleague together with one of the consultant obstetricians and one of our DSNs who had developed a special interest in the subject. Pregnant ladies with diabetes and their partners were seen there at very frequent intervals throughout the woman's pregnancy. This is an essential exercise aimed at the outcome of a successful delivery of a normal, healthy baby, and a happy mother and father as a result. An equally essential exercise was steering people with diabetes and failing kidney function towards the point of renal replace-ment therapy by dialysis and/or transplantation, and keeping them as well as possible on the way there to give them the best chance of success.

Chris and I had been running our Joint Diabetes Renal Clinic for well over twenty-five years. I met up with him soon after we were both appointed consultants, which occurred at about the same time, and suggested the idea. I had had experience of the importance of diabetologists and nephrologists running things together in my five years as a senior registrar on the Diabetes Unit at Guy's Hospital, where, among other things, I had been responsible for those of our patients with chronic diabetic kidney disease. I would attend the weekly renal meetings to discuss the patients and plan their management with our consultant nephrology colleagues. Chris had been enthusiastic about the idea of teaming up, and remained so for all the enjoyable years we were to work together. Our Joint Diabetes Renal Clinic in Eastbourne seemed to have been appreciated by patients and their GPs alike, and we were proud to have an article we had written about the theory and practice of our joint clinic published in a national journal and labelled 'best practice'.

However, I have to say, not all kidney specialists in the country were convinced by the idea of joint clinics. But it seemed to me that they were all ones who were not run-ning such a clinic! I think they imagined that it was not an efficient use of consultants' time, and that communication could proceed in a perfectly satisfactory manner via the usual method of letters sent between the specialists concerned. As far as Chris and I were concerned, the benefits for our patients were significant. For a start, our patients did not have to travel the difficult twenty-mile journey to the Renal Unit in Brighton to be seen each time. Chris came to us. We believed that such a clinic very much optimised communications, management and support for patients and their families, tailoring medical care to a patient-sensitive approach. The joint clinic provided a one-stop, multi-disciplinary team approach which was cost-effective as well as having the advantage of introducing the patient and his / her family to the nephrologist in the context of their past medical and psychosocial history. To put it another way, I knew all my patients very well (and they knew me) and as a result Chris got to know them (and they got to know him) quickly as well. I like to think that all of this took a lot of the fear away for these patients who were facing the very daunting prospect of a life on dialysis or a kidney transplant, if their lives were to be saved. They were not afraid to ask us any questions they needed to. In turn, they knew we were listening to them together.

Although Stan seemed keen for the chance to prolong his life beyond the point where his kidneys had failed to a fatal degree, he never reached that point. Sadly, we heard one day that he had died suddenly. I never found out the details of how he had died, but suspect he may have had another stroke, having suffered a 'mini' stroke a year or two before. Diabetic kidney disease is associated with a much higher risk of 'vascular events' – heart attacks and strokes in particular – and it is not unusual, in spite of the best care we can give with blood sugar-, blood pressure- and cholesterol-lowering drugs, for people with diabetes and kidney failure to be carried off by one of these attacks first, before their kidneys fail completely.

27

Listening to Complaints

ONE DAY I RECEIVED AN UNEXPECTED TELEPHONE CALL from a manager in a primary care trust (PCT) outside our region. 'Is that Dr Bending?' he enquired. 'Please forgive me for phoning, but I have been given your name as somebody who may be able to help us. You are a diabetes specialist, I understand?'

'Yes,' I said.

'And you deal with diabetic foot problems?'

'Of course,' I replied.

'Excellent,' was his response.

'Go on,' I said, somewhat surprised and waiting to hear what this was all about.

'We've got a bit of a problem,' the manager continued. 'One of our chiropodists has treated a patient with a diabetic foot problem which subsequently became infected and then gangrenous. The patient's lower leg had to be amputated. The chiropodist will have to face a disciplinary hearing which will most likely result in his dismissal from his present post and probably in erasure by his professional body as well, barring him from practice in the future. But before that we have to go through the hoops of arranging an Independent Review hearing. We need an expert consultant advisor to sit on the review panel. Would you be able to help?'

'I'd be happy to do what I can,' I said, taking it all in. 'But since this is a professional competency issue, don't you think you should have a podiatrist on the review panel as well?'

'What a good idea!' came back the manager, with alarming naïveity, I couldn't help thinking. 'Do you have one of those?'

'Yes' – I hesitated – 'but wouldn't it be wiser if the person concerned was not somebody whom I work with on a daily basis?'

'Oh, right. Can you recommend anybody?' I gave him the name of Alethea Foster, chief podiatrist at the world-famous Diabetes Foot Clinic at King's College Hospital in London.

I picked Ali up at the railway station in my car and we drove together to the PCT offices. The Independent Review was held in the rather chilly boardroom. The chairperson was a mature lady with blue-rinsed white hair, who was accompanied by a senior manager and a lay representative, a man who had been a train driver all his life and still wore his ASLEF badge on the lapel of his jacket to prove it. After introducing ourselves, we were offered a cup of coffee and sat around the boardroom table. The chairlady introduced the reason for the review and gave the story, reading from a script she had been provided with. When the process for the review had been agreed, the patient was invited to step into the room. He was accompanied by his wife for support.

The man was a sixty-one-year-old retired school teacher with a history of type 1 diabetes of forty-eight years' duration. His diabetes had been complicated by retinopathy, resulting in the recent loss of vision in one eye. He appeared pale and tired and walked in to the room swivelling his hip as he dragged forward the prosthetic right leg which had been fitted following the below-knee amputation he had recently undergone. He bravely talked us through the traumatic last few months he had suffered, leading up to the amputation of his leg. He made it quite clear that, as far as he was concerned, this should never have happened. He blamed the podiatrist and wanted to ensure that he would not be able to cause the same harm to anybody else in the future. He wanted him struck off. He also wanted an unreserved apology from the primary care trust and appropriate compensation for the loss he had suffered, although he stressed to us that the reason for his complaint was not financial benefit. His wife did not speak during her husband's presentation to us, although she was clearly supporting him in every detail. When the patient had finished, the chair thanked the man and his wife sincerely before they left and assured them that a full report would come out of the day's proceedings and that they would be the first to receive a copy of it. They left grateful to have had the hearing they had received.

After a short break, we then sat down to examine the medical records. Having had the opportunity to review the records in detail before the hearing, I took the lead in explaining to the other non-medical panel members what they contained. It had come to light from these that the patient had both impairment of the sensory nerves in his lower legs and of the blood circulation to his feet, although neither the patient himself nor, most worryingly, the primary care team looking after him appeared to have been aware of this fact. His practice nurse had referred him to a community podiatrist because she had noted a thickening and discolouration of his toenails. The original referral, however, had gone missing. A further handwritten referral was made twenty-three days later, after a telephone request to the surgery by the patient, but this referral gave no indication of the clinical nature of the problem (the patient not having been reviewed in surgery).

The podiatrist was then invited in to the room. He was a man in his forties, ashen-faced and accompanied by a representative from the UK Society of Chiropodists and Podiatrists. He told us that the referral he had received gave no indication of urgency but that, nevertheless, he had seen the patient within two weeks of this second referral. It was the first time he had met the patient. He had diagnosed that the man was developing an infection of the foot, with the skin and tissues starting to break down and pus collecting under the thickened toenails. The pus needed immediate draining, which involved him having to cut back the overlying area of the nail plate. He explained to the lay members of the panel that this is a procedure which can sometimes be painful, but for which a local anaesthetic is not usually given. This is because the presence of fluid under the nail lifts the nail plate, which can therefore be cut back with less discomfort to the patient than the pain of undergoing a 'ring block' of local anaesthetic (being injected around the base of the toe). Furthermore, while the presence of pus under the nail is painful, its drainage usually eases pain very quickly, giving the patient relief.

The podiatrist told us that, following the immediate treatment he had given, he had recommended that the patient visit his general practitioner for antibiotic treatment and subsequent regular dressing by the practice nurse. The GP's surgery was next door to the podiatry clinic. The podiatrist did not arrange a routine follow-up appointment but asked the patient to report back to his GP or to himself if there was any sign of deterioration. The podiatrist said that he had sent a report to the patient's GP, but this had never been found and the podiatrist did not have a copy of his letter.

As it turned out, the patient did not report to his GP for antibiotics as instructed. Nor did he present himself for a follow-up review by his GP or the podiatrist, as the podiatrist had asked him to do. The foot developed an infection and gangrene, which ascended up the foot to the leg. The eventual result of this was that the patient required a below-knee amputation, which was performed by a general surgeon whom he saw privately. The patient had complained that the podiatrist had not provided adequate care, that he had been exposed to a severely painful surgical procedure (the cutting back of the nails) without explanation or anaesthetic and, furthermore, that the podiatrist had been responsible for causing his foot problems and subsequent leg amputation.

People with diabetes have a twenty-times increased risk of having to undergo the amputation of a whole or part of a limb – invariably the lower limb – compared to the rest of the population. And the 'rest of the population' includes all those life-long heavy smokers who also develop diseases of the blood vessels supplying the legs as a result – peripheral vascular disease, as it is called. No surgeon ever undertakes an amputation lightly and they are usually performed only once the development of infection and gangrene has reached the stage where the infection is starting to spread throughout the patient's body (septicaemia) and they will lose their life if the gangrenous limb is not removed.

The extremely distressing process of undergoing amputation is often followed by denial and grief over the loss of both body image and function. Anger and blame for causing the amputation may be directed at those health-care professionals who were involved in the treatment of the affected limb. While this recurrent need to allocate blame is not a new phenomenon, it now occurs in the context of an increasingly litigation-prone climate. Claims against vascular surgeons, for example, were shown to have risen four-fold in a recent ten-year period. It is clear that lawsuits are filed not just for financial reasons, but also because people feel abandoned and aggrieved. Podiatrists are often blamed when a person

with diabetes undergoes amputation. Although many complaints are settled locally and quickly, there seems to be an
increasing climate of litigation against podiatrists, who may
be blamed for causing ulcers, gangrene or amputation. The
understanding of the work of podiatrists is frequently poor
among patients and other health-care practitioners, and
consequently podiatrists may be held directly responsible
for the amputation due to ignorance about their scope of
practice. Community podiatrists, who often work in isola-
tion, both in a literal and wider professional sense, appear
to be especially at risk of such accusations.

Ali and I looked at each other as we heard the podiatrist
give his side of the story. He was clearly under severe strain,
but nevertheless remained polite and dignified during the
whole process. We could see that he was a caring professional, who had only done his best for the patient at the
time he had seen him. It was also clear that, for whatever
reason, the patient had not followed his advice about seeing
his GP for antibiotics immediately after, and nor had he
reported back for regular dressings or review when the
situation started to deteriorate. When he had been with
us, we had not asked the patient directly why it was that
he had not followed the advice which he had been given
by the podiatrist. I suspect he may not have been able to
answer this question clearly.

After the podiatrist had left the room, the review panel
commenced its deliberations. Ali and I had not a little

difficulty explaining our views to the other members of the panel, which were that, at the time that he saw the patient, the treatment and advice given by the podiatrist had been completely appropriate and, furthermore, we were of the opinion that he could not be held responsible for the subsequent deterioration in the man's condition and the ultimate loss of his limb. The senior manager in particular seemed aghast by what we were telling them. He had assumed that the podiatrist was guilty, even before the man had had the chance to prove his innocence. Eventually, the rest of the panel understood that the podiatrist had not been to blame for the course of events which led to the amputation of the man's leg. This was made clear in the Independent Review's report. The panel's conclusion was that the cutting back of the nails was an appropriate treatment but it did go on to criticise failures of communication between the podiatrist, GP and practice nurse. The review panel gave guidance about the importance of careful record keeping and storing and also ways in which improvements in communications with patients could be made. The panel also advised the primary care trust (PCT), for whom the podiatrist worked, to establish written guidelines for the treatment, referral and follow-up of diabetic foot patients. The podiatrist was free to continue practising.

28

Listening to Another Complaint

A COUPLE OF MONTHS LATER I WAS ASKED TO BE THE expert consultant advisor on another complaint about a podiatrist's treatment of a patient with diabetes. This time the patient was a fifty-three-year-old man with type 2 diabetes of eight years' duration, who had developed a neuropathic foot ulcer (caused by the loss of function of his sensory nerves) which healed in three months. Following this he had had no contact with the local podiatry service for nine months but had then telephoned a community podiatrist complaining of a new foot ulcer. She advised him over the phone to see his GP for antibiotics. She also saw him herself the same day, when she learned that he had not in fact visited the GP following his telephone call to her. His reason for this was that 'it takes a week to get an appointment'. He had also visited the Accident and Emergency Department of a local hospital two days previously, but had not waited to be seen. The podiatrist cleaned, debrided (cut out the dead tissue) and dressed the ulcer and offered frequent appointments over the next three months, during which period two other ulcers on the patient's feet developed and healed.

Although the primary ulcer failed to heal, the podiatrist recorded that she could find no clinical evidence of infection and the patient was also seen by two other podiatrists, on single occasions, neither of whom felt the need for referral. The patient's memory of this time, however, was that the foot was swollen and that his partner had commented on the fact that the foot was malodorous. Three months later the foot suddenly deteriorated. The podiatrist obtained an X-ray referral from the local consultant diabetologist, although the patient felt that this was only because he had repeatedly asked her to organise this. He commented that the podiatrist had neither organised, nor learnt how to organise, an X-ray before. The diabetologist saw the X-ray and arranged to admit the patient to hospital the same day. The toe required amputation. Four months after the amputation the patient had received no podiatry follow-up. He complained bitterly that he had lost his toe because of poor podiatry care and a failure to refer him to a specialist centre.

Ali and I met up again for the second Independent Review hearing after local resolution had failed, the structure of which was much the same as the previous hearing. This time, we could find no fault in the timing, regularity and appropriateness of the treatment offered by the podiatrist, but we were concerned that she had been working in a very isolated manner. She was unsure about the mechanism for obtaining microbiology (swabs) and X-rays of a toe and rarely saw the consultant diabetologist or other members of the diabetes team. There were no mechanisms for ensuring follow-up appointments for high-risk patients and the podiatry service depended on the patients themselves making further appointments. There was no system for contacting or recalling high-risk diabetic patients who failed to attend an appointment. The panel made recommendations to the PCT relating to community podiatrists working alone in the care of people with diabetes.

As I drove Ali back to the local station to catch her train to London, I said, 'My word! Are these episodes with patients' foot-care complaints increasing so much?'

'I'm afraid so, Jeremy,' she replied. 'It seems to be the result of many more people with diabetes being cared for solely in general practice, by doctors and nurses who are not trained or experienced in recognising and managing these serious complications. As we said in our Independent Review reports, both these patients should have been referred urgently to the local hospital multidisciplinary specialist diabetes footcare clinic. But, as we know, there is great pressure on GPs *not* to refer patients to hospital these days, in an attempt to save money. It's all very sad!'

The anger which patients with diabetes quite commonly feel following lower extremity amputation can lead to complaints and litigation directed at those perceived to be at fault. All health-care professionals are at risk of being complained about (whether justly or unjustly) but podiatrists appear to be especially and increasingly at risk from scenarios such as these. Accusations that a podiatrist was responsible for a catastrophe may be founded on lack of understanding and poor communication. It is, therefore, essential for podiatrists to explain treatments and their rationale – particularly at the first encounter with a diabetic foot patient. Problems are exacerbated by the fact that diabetic feet can deteriorate with alarming rapidity, sometimes within a few hours of a break in the skin appearing.

As well as having lost the sensation in their feet, many diabetes patients with foot problems also have impaired eyesight (retinopathy) and are unable to see their feet clearly. Patients may thus be unaware that they have a foot problem, or that the condition of the foot is deteriorating. They may be unaware of the practical implications of protective sensation loss and its dangers, even though the potential problems may have been discussed with them many times during their diabetic life and diabetes footcare advice reinforced regularly. This failure on the part of people with diabetes to comprehend how diabetic foot problems develop or to perceive that they are at risk may be due to a genuine lack of understanding, but is very often associated with a profound sense of denial – well known to be a major factor in many patients who come to grief with diabetic foot problems. They can see that they have a problem developing but tell themselves that the problem does not exist. The analogy I sometimes used was that of the woman with a fungating cancerous tumour growing through the skin of her breast which she has been unable to acknowledge to herself, let alone bring to the attention of her husband.

Part of the grieving process following a serious illness, amputation or death involves anger and denial, as already discussed, and a need to allocate blame. Patients may feel safer if they can believe their problem was a one-off disaster which was the fault of someone else. This may reflect, perhaps, an unconscious inability to admit that they themselves may have had a part to play in not avoiding the outcome. They thereby deny responsibility for self-care, as well as the possibility that they may still be at risk of further problems, including the loss of the remaining toes or limb. Furthermore, neuropathy (the damage to the sensory nerves caused by diabetes) has very profound effects on diabetic patients: they do not perceive their feet as a problem when they are not in pain, and the lack of feeling gives them a very abnormal view of the 'boundaries of self'. In other words, they may not feel responsible for the feet they cannot feel, and they will not feel pain or unpleasant symptoms until their foot problems are very advanced. In a symptom-led health-care system, this failure to complain or report foot problems because they are not painful frequently leads to disaster.

The loss of a limb has been compared to the loss of a spouse. The clear visual memories of that which is lost, and the strong sense of its persisting presence, are manifest in the amputee as the phantom limb. The anxiety, depression and sexual problems which may develop are often related not only to the type of loss (leg compared to toe in the above examples), but also to the personal vulnerability of each individual patient. In other words, the premorbid personality of a patient influences their ability to cope with such a situation, and podiatrists and other health-care professionals should be aware that amputees with a long-standing tendency to anxiety and depression ('sensitisers') have been shown to cope less well – as do those (usually men) who show little evidence of distress at the time of amputation ('avoiders'). Problems following amputation can be prevented by information, advice and emotional support prior to surgery. Patients should be warned that the sensation of a phantom limb, which can be painful, may persist for a while. Early recognition of any issues is important in reducing possible long-term psychological morbidity. Every patient should be asked how they feel following amputation and should be encouraged to discuss problems. Involving the family in this is helpful to both. Additionally, meeting other amputees can reassure patients that it is possible to live with disability.

By understanding the reasons which lead diabetic patients smitten with the tragedy of amputation to complain and undertake litigation, we believe a service can be better equipped to minimise such complaint. The development of agreed guidelines and care pathways should result in a much-improved podiatry service and reduce dissatisfaction directed at diabetes carers, among whom community podiatrists appear to be particularly at risk. Most importantly, by providing support and counselling aimed at preventing and recognising the psychological morbidity of this condition, diabetes teams can give better care to patients at the profoundly tragic point of surgical amputation.

29

Listening to the Candidates

THE ROYAL COLLEGE OF PHYSICIANS OF LONDON IS the college which represents all consultant physicians in England and Wales and, with its sister colleges in Edinburgh and Glasgow, in the United Kingdom as a whole. The college is an august institution, founded in 1518 by a royal charter from King Henry VIII, and therefore is now 500 years old. At its foundation, the leading physicians of the time wanted the power to grant licences to those qualified to practise medicine and to punish unqualified practitioners and those engaging in malpractice. As the founding charter decreed, this college would 'curb the audacity of those wicked men who shall profess medicine more for the sake of their avarice than from the assurance of any good conscience, whereby very many inconveniences may ensue to the rude and credulous populace'. The first president of the college wanted to found an academic body for physicians, rather than a trade guild of the kind which regulated surgeons and apothecaries. Physicians were seen as the educated elite of the medical world: a degree was usually required to gain a licence. Candidates for fellowship underwent an oral examination to demonstrate that they were 'groundedly learned' (classically educated) in addition to their knowledge of medicine.

Geographically, placed as it is on the side of Regents Park in London, the facilities of the present-day college favour those physicians who live and practise in the capital. Apart from infrequent visits to the college to listen to an evening lecture, which was difficult for me to arrange with my clinical commitments, the journey by train from the South Coast taking the best part of ninety minutes each way, I was never in a position to use such facilities of the college as the fellows' rooms and libraries. It is true to say that the college was seen by many district general hospital physicians like myself to be the domain of academic and politically orientated physicians located in and around London. This, in spite of the fact that the college has done its best coming into the twenty-first century to take a lead role in contributing to medical and governmental advisory matters.

The one aspect in which the Royal College of Physicians UK has had particular success is in the conduct and development of its professional examination, the Membership of the Royal College of Physicians, or MRCP(UK). The MRCP is the examination which all doctors need to pass if they are to continue with a career in specialist hospital medicine and, ultimately, to become consultant physicians. In order to become a hospital medical registrar and to progress in a specialist registrar training post, it is a necessary hurdle to first pass the membership exam. The MRCP London Diploma was first introduced in 1859, and has remained the cornerstone of establishing a candidate's fitness to practise specialist internal medicine ever since. Examinations for licences and membership remain rigorous and academically based, which is reflected in the MRCP. I passed the MRCP when I was a senior house officer in 1977, three years after qualifying as a doctor. The award of Fellowship of the College (FRCP) only came, as with my other contemporaries, in 1993, when I was already six years into my consultant post and after nomination by my local consultant peers. At that time, the MRCP examination consisted of two parts; a written part 1 followed by a part 2 comprising both written and practical clinical assessments. All the parts of the exam, as might be expected from a professional entrance examination, were difficult, but part 2 was especially so. The exam was undoubtedly arduous, but most candidates were at least aware that the clinical exam also had an old school, unpredictable performance element to it. It was clear to many, and eventually the college itself, that the MRCP examination needed to be brought up to date and made to demonstrate high standards which were both reproducible and transparent.

I had been a consultant examiner of the old MRCP examination since 1999. In 2001, the colleges of physicians in the UK finally took steps towards bringing the MRCP exam up to date. This did not meet with approval in all quarters, and, not surprisingly, many of the older examiners viewed any attempt at 'tinkering' with what was considered to be the hallowed ground of the MRCP as 'unthinkable'. Nevertheless, the academic committees met and a new standardised exam was finally born. The clinical part of the examination became the Practical Assessment of Clinical Examination Skills – or PACES, as the exam is now commonly known. Along with all the other examiners, I was invited to the College of Physicians in London to be instructed in the conduct of the new exam. The packed lecture theatre was listening to one of the presenters on the stage explain that the candidate in Station 2 (where they would be assessed at history taking) would be given a referral letter from a GP setting out the patient's presenting problem, which they then had to address with the patient. At that moment, the back door of the lecture theatre flew open and my examiner-brother Michael, a consultant physician and nephrologist, came crashing in late as usual and threw up his hand.

Presenter: 'Question at the back?'

Dr Michael Bending: 'Can you please tell us; will the letter be legible or illegible?' The audience fell about laughing but the very serious presenter on the stage continued without reply!

The MRCP PACES clinical exam now consists of five twenty-minute 'stations', around which each candidate has to proceed with military timing. The stations not only assess each doctor's ability to carry out examinations of body systems, such as the chest and abdomen and the cardiovascular and neurological systems – as well as their ability to put their findings from these into logical context and discuss plans for investigation and treatment of the conditions they find – but they also include two so-called 'listening stations', in which the candidates are observed taking a history from a patient and conducting interviews with patients and/or relatives. In addition to providing a test of the candidate's ability to communicate professionally and sympathetically with ill patients and relatives, these stations act as a vehicle for assessing their conduct when 'breaking bad news' and dealing with ethical dilemmas. In this context, I believe that the specialist medical examination has been groundbreaking in seeking to put the importance of a doctor's bedside manner and their ability to demonstrate compassion on an equal footing with their factual medical knowledge, and it has gained recognition around the world for this achievement.

Station 4 of the PACES clinical exam, which examines the candidate's ability to communicate and their grasp of ethics, involves him or her being watched grappling with difficult interviews with patients or relatives. There are many different scenarios in each exam but examples include being faced by the mother of a patient who has cornered the doctor in the corridor and wants to know the cause of her thirty-year-old son's jaundice. The candidate is told she/he has been looking after the son, who has developed hepatitis (inflammation of the liver) as a presenting feature of AIDS, but that this man, who has admitted to unsafe homosexual activity about which his family is unaware, has said that he only agrees to his family being told in general terms about the causes of liver failure. Another scenario is the very common one of explaining to a relative visiting from afar why it is that their elderly parent has developed a stroke, why she is not getting better and why it is she is not able to be fed immediately and conventionally. These scenarios, and many others, really do examine the candidate doctors' professionalism and ability to communicate openly and sympathetically with patients and relatives.

Like other examiners, I was initially unsure about the fact that, in some of the stations, real patients had been replaced by surrogates – secretaries, specialist nurses or sometimes even professional actors – who played the role of the patient or relative. My early doubt about whether this was perhaps not a little trendy has been assuaged by the realisation that these surrogates are invariably excellent in their roles and, furthermore, are able to reproduce the part they are playing in a consistent way from one candidate to another, without becoming tired or ill as the exam progresses, as was often unavoidably the case when real patients were used. The exam is now respected worldwide, the written exam being held in thirty-four countries and the PACES clinical exam in fourteen different countries, including parts of Africa and the Near and Far East.

In 2003, I was appointed as a senior examiner and a chair of the MRCP exams. An honour though this was considered to be, in reality the role was in many ways even more arduous than being an individual examiner. It entailed collaborating with the hospital hosting a particular exam before, during and after each exam; ensuring that the exam proceeded smoothly, to time and without hitch; and keeping up to twenty-two other examiner consultant colleagues happy and in order. I found that the exam went smoothest if the other examiners were able to relax and enjoy themselves while still taking the running of the exam seriously, since we all realised that the need to pass the exam was a very serious matter indeed, personally and professionally, for the candidates themselves.

It was always a pleasant opportunity to be able to meet up with and get to know consultant physician colleagues from around the UK, some of whom I have continued to keep in contact with, and to know that they were all experiencing similar problems in their own corners of the NHS. After the hard work, we would have the opportunity to talk and meet over evening dinner. On the last night, when it was my job to thank the local team who had organised the exam, as well as my fellow examiners, I always tried to take the opportunity to tell a few jokes and lighten the occasion. Whenever I would announce to my junior medical team at home that I was going to be away for a few days (to London, Middlesbrough, Glasgow, or wherever – hospitals all over the UK now host the exam simultaneously), I was often aware that they had the impression that I was off on some 'jolly' at the expense of the candidates! I made a point of explaining to them that, not only was I acting as an examiner unpaid, it was physically pretty hard work, which involved standing for up to eight hours a day examining.

30

Listening to Each Other

AS A TEAM, ALTHOUGH WE WERE ALL WORKED OFF our feet, we nevertheless knew the importance of making time to meet together and 'listen to each other'. At the simplest level, this meant that any of the DSNs or other colleagues could walk into my office, or that of my consultant colleague, whether we were consulting with a patient or not, and ask for help, advice or an opinion on something. Similarly, I would certainly not hesitate to walk in to one of my colleagues' rooms to ask for their help or support if I needed it. Our main weekly diabetes team meeting was held on a Tuesday lunchtime when we all got together to discuss the issues around the management of individual patients and our service in general. This meeting was usually accompanied by a sandwich lunch provided by a drug-company representative from their educational budget. Whilst we were always very grateful for the lunch, it was often very difficult to make the rep stick to the allotted fifteen-minute slot for promoting their drug and to get them to leave the meeting after this, so as to allow enough time for the team to talk together alone and in confidence.

The outpatient clinics were conducted along the same lines: the specialist registrars knew that they were encouraged to come into my room to discuss any patient or management problem which they might need to. Halfway through the endocrinology clinic on a Thursday afternoon, the doctors would meet up in my room – myself, my two consultant colleagues, our specialist registrars and our clinic nurses – to discuss the new endocrinology patients we had all just seen. In recognition of the complexity of many of these new endocrinology patient problems, and the time needed to unravel them, forty minutes was allocated to each of two new patients for each doctor between 2.00 and 3.20 pm. At 3.20 p.m. we would get together to discuss these patients, which provided both an opportunity for clinical guidance and an educational session for our younger colleagues, before resuming the clinic at 3.30 p.m. to carry on seeing follow-up patients. There was actually an empty ten-minute slot in the clinic timetable to allow us a break for a cup of tea and patient discussion. You might not be surprised to hear that, after this system had been running for many years, I received an email one day from a new manager, who was green around the gills, telling me that he had been reviewing our particular clinic template and had found a gap between patients at 3.20 p.m. and 3.30 p.m. on the Thursday afternoon endocrinology clinic. He was wondering whether this could not be filled with an additional new patient slot? You can imagine my polite reply informing him what the gap was there for!

Every Friday at 1 p.m. we would also meet up as a team with Dr Stephen Bangert, our consultant chemical pathologist colleague, and his senior biochemist colleague to discuss the week's interesting endocrinology problems. They were always very keen to come over to the Diabetes Centre seminar room for these sessions and would provide us with stimulating and thoughtful ideas of their own. In this process, they would learn about patients that we might have been having problems coming to a diagnosis with, and the specialist endocrinological tests that we were planning to bring the patients in for, which we would need their laboratory service skills with.

The concept of 'listening to each other' was not only something which we applied to ourselves as a team, but also something which we developed with our diabetes patients. We knew instinctively from our training that group sessions were a very important and useful way of helping people with diabetes come to terms with their condition and to learn about how to manage it. They would learn not only from us, but also from other people with the same diabetes-related problems that they were experiencing. This applied as much to the younger people with type 1 diabetes as it did to the older patients with type 2 diabetes. While this was an approach embraced by many of our patients with diabetes, it was not something that everyone was keen on. A proportion of people invited to attend a group session would politely decline, indicating that this was not for them. Within a group, there was always the person who was generally silent and hesitant about joining in. It was a challenge to encourage these people to 'open up' and take part, sometimes by politely requesting the more vociferous members of the group to 'pipe down' to allow this to happen. It was always interesting to observe, however, how some members of a group who had been tentative about taking part at the start of the group sessions were the ones who enthusiastically acknowledged how much they had learned and appreciated the sessions when they came to an end.

When Pari retired, Sally took over as our lead diabetes specialist nurse. She had not been a DSN all that long, but, like Pari, she was an excellent nurse and also turned out to be an excellent leader. Even prior to taking up her job as lead DSN, Sally had been instrumental in establishing our 'SADIE' course. This acronym stood for 'Skill for Adjusting Diet and Insulin in Eastbourne' (or East Sussex, as it later became). This was an intensive course delivered over a six-week period, one day each week, for groups of people with type 1 insulin-dependent diabetes, providing them with an update in all aspects of diabetes treatment and management. The format was not about lecturing to patients, however, but that of an interactive group approach, with no more than about eight patients in each group. People found this immensely supportive and interesting. In general, the participants found it very helpful listening to each other's stories and problems, and being offered expert guidance as to how each of them might tackle these issues for themselves. I know this because they said so in their feedback and due to the fact that there was a very long waiting list for people wanting to get a place on the course. When something is as good and helpful as this, word gets around quickly. We were so proud when the course was given a national award for its success by NICE, the National Institute for Health and Care Excellence.

With Janet, our senior diabetes specialist dietitian, who had also been a core member of the SADIE group, Sally and I went on to set up our insulin-pump service for people with diabetes. In my time at Guy's Hospital I had been deeply involved with the development of the insulin pump, which used a small battery-operated pump to infuse insulin continuously under the skin, thereby significantly ironing out the – usually wide – fluctuations in blood insulin and glucose levels that a number of injections a day inevitably produced. The unit had invented the technique and used it in the research we undertook, which looked at the importance of tight blood glucose control in the prevention of the development and progression of diabetes-related complications – particularly those of the eye and kidney. I had written my doctoral MD thesis on this subject. After being appointed as the first consultant specialising in diabetes and endocrinology in Eastbourne, I had so much to do establishing the diabetes team and setting up an endocrinology service from scratch that I made the conscious decision not to offer a complete insulin-pump service in the early years.

There were a number of pump-treated patients whom I looked after, but I knew that to offer the pump service properly I would need facilities that we just did not have in those days – especially enough dedicated DSNs to cover the hours this intensive treatment required. So, it was exciting to arrive at the point when we could start to offer such a structured service, and Sally, Janet and I chose to deliver the initial teaching to small groups of patients, which was a way of making the process efficient in terms of teaching time.

31

Divide and Rule

MEDICINE IN GENERAL IS ABOUT TEAMWORK. IT HAS to be: patients' lives are at risk, as is their well-being. This is no more true than in diabetes care, where we are all rightly proud of our tradition of working as a team. The work of our team was always structured with the person with diabetes themself as its central member. The diabetes specialist team included not only the two (and later three) consultants who specialised in diabetes, but also two specialist registrars (the doctors in training to become consultant specialists in diabetes and endocrinology), five diabetes specialist nurses, our diabetes specialist dietitian and podiatrists, not to mention the team of secretaries and administrative staff which running a diabetes centre requires. Other members of the extended diabetes team who came in and out as required included our consultant vascular surgeon colleagues, ophthalmologists, radiologists and orthopaedic consultants.

The diabetes specialist team may not have had to function in the same way as, say, a surgical team – gowned up in green strips and masks; ensuring the surgeon is handed all the instruments he needs at the correct time, and in the right order, as the used swabs are accounted for, with none left behind in error in the patient's abdomen, and the anaesthetist gets on with monitoring the level of the patient's unconsciousness and the fluctuation in their vital signs. But the need for team cohesion, although very different from the operating-theatre scenario, is no less critical for providing well-being to patients in the long run.

Providing care and support to a person with diabetes also means having to repeat much of the advice given to them, sometimes at every visit, throughout their life with the condition. 'Diabetes education' is the term commonly used for this process, although I sometimes felt that it was a rather condescending label. (In the United States, diabetes specialist nurses are called 'diabetes nurse *educators*'!) It is vital, in this process, that the information given to people with diabetes is up to date and correct, and that the patient is given consistent advice by every professional they see. It can be very discouraging for a person with diabetes to be given incorrect advice by, say, a GP practice nurse, which has to be politely corrected during a visit to the Diabetes Centre.

It is one thing building up a team, challenging though that can often be, but it is quite another thing keeping it together. I used to say that it was like taking two steps forward and one step back all the time, as people came and went and had to be replaced. At every step, if a member of the team moved on or retired, we had to defend the need for a replacement and fiercely protect the funding. I used to feel that the managers' attitude to us was very often professionally insulting. Their questioning about the need for what we were doing, and their lack of insight and understanding about the purpose of the service we were working to provide, at times bordered on the offensive. It showed that they had no real understanding about our service and, I have to say, in most cases did not really care.

But the need for the diabetes specialist team had nothing to do with building up an empire: it was the desperate need for providing specialised services not only to all the patients who needed it – and indeed had a right to it – but also to the other health-care colleagues who required the support and education. These included hospital doctors (junior but also not so junior), GPs, practice nurses, district nurses, school teachers – the list is long. You would have thought that, at a time when an explosion in the number of people with diabetes was (and still is) occurring and considering the fact that the direct costs of diabetes already consume something like ten per cent of our total NHS budget, the need for diabetes specialist teams in every hospital and district would be self-evident? But not a bit of it! The threats to the diabetes specialist team came from all directions, including from within our own hospital trust.

The fact that our sister hospital in Hastings had only a relatively small diabetes team and far less-developed services was an excuse for the managers and outside management consultants – private management advisors who were parachuted in to the trust from time to time to make recommendations at the cost of millions of pounds – to repeatedly question every bit of the service we had built up, from consultants down to secretaries and admin assistants and back up again. 'How come you've got so many more secretary hours per consultant head than they have in Hastings?' their cry would go up.

'It's bleeding obvious!' I would reply (or words to that effect). 'We run a much more developed service and very many more clinics. In any case, the secretaries are not just typists. They answer the Diabetes Centre phones and act as receptionists at the same time as undertaking all their other secretarial duties. The letter-typing service they provide is not just for our two-and-a-bit consultants, but for the registrars, DSNs, dietitians, podiatrists, and other members of the team. But you persist in setting a quota of 0.8 of a secretary for each consultant (which is what was allowed for a single-handed consultant providing a service alone). Where did this fraction of a number come from and who invented it? It's clearly irrelevant to an extended team of health-care professionals!' The managers were never happy with this reply. They were only ever interested in saving money, not in the service. (I can't remember when I ever heard a manager actually make me aware that she/he understood what we did and what the quality of service we were striving to achieve was.) The attempt to compare one end of our trust with the other was just a convenient way of trying to reduce all to the lowest common denominator.

With time and hard work, the diabetes team was built up to include five DSNs, in addition to our senior diabetes specialist dietitian, a part-time dietitian and two or three podiatrists who shared the load. Somehow, as the team expanded, we were still able to house all the members in the original building, which had been built from scratch using money I had raised in the early years from charitable donations, patient groups and the community. We did so by creatively using the space we had – sometimes adding a wall down the middle of one of the larger rooms to make it into two offices for the use of two DSNs, so that they each had space to consult with their patients in private. But the heart of a diabetes centre is not the building, it is the team within it. The Diabetes Centre is a focus for diabetes care, acting as the centre of gravity from which this is provided.

It is a fact that the advent of the diabetes specialist nurse – who was the first of all the specialist nurses in the UK to come into existence – has been the most important development in the care of people with diabetes since the discovery of insulin: I always used to say this and have written as such on more than one occasion. The DSN has the time and commitment to support patients with their diabetes. If the doctor-led diabetes clinics were places for *problem-finding* (such as ascertaining whether a patient needed help with understanding their diabetes, with improving their diabetes control, or with on-going treatment for a diabetic foot problem or any other complication), the Diabetes Centre was the place for *problem-solving*. It was where all the on-going care and support for people with diabetes was delivered. The development of diabetes specialist teams throughout the UK in the last forty or more years is something to be greatly proud of and is the envy of many other countries.

The most depressing scenario of all over the past decade or two has been the one played out on a national scale. The need for greater involvement by general practitioners in the care of people with diabetes – which is admirable and necessary in its own right – has been pushed through by recent successive governments not as an addition to specialist care, but in the (unspoken) hope that it will replace the hospital-based teams and thereby save money. It won't, of course. There will be a rise in complications and hospital admissions from people receiving primary care for their diabetes only. Remember the problem about diabetes footcare discussed earlier? Many of my GP colleagues were non-political in their professional practice and did a good job, knowing when to ask for help and referring patients to the hospital for specialist care when it was needed and appropriate. The dangerous ones were the small group of often vociferous GPs who were convinced that they knew everything, and indeed more about diabetes and its management than their hospital specialist colleagues. They spent a lot of their time shouting loudly that they were messiahs for the future for diabetes care, and no doubt impressing the primary care managers, if not their more down-to-earth GP colleagues, in the process. These GPs frequently exhibited what I often called 'the arrogance of ignorance'.

It is also true that governments have recently spent millions of pounds on rewarding GPs for doing basic things like taking a patient's blood pressure, measuring their HbA1c blood test or asking if they feel depressed. This top-down approach to dictating care through the carrot of extra remuneration has been responsible for a large divide having been created between hospital-based specialist teams and GP practices. The fact is that GPs are now paid large amounts of money for these so-called 'Quof' (quality outcome framework) points and that these have become a significant part of their income. This also means that GPs are actively dissuaded from making referrals to hospital specialists in general, in the hope that money will be saved – another part of the process of 'divide and rule'. What sort of way is that to conduct high-quality patient-centred medicine? Even basic good practice should mean that these clinical activities are undertaken anyway, without the practitioner having to be persuaded of the need for them by financial enticements. In any case, the system which was set up to persuade GPs to become more involved in the care of people with diabetes on their lists measures 'process' but does not in fact measure 'outcome'. That would come from looking at the numbers of patients under their care who still undergo amputation, go blind, suffer kidney failure, and so on.

It is outrageous that the points awarded to GPs as a financial incentive ('points mean prizes!') can be gained if the measures have been made by anyone; not necessarily by the GPs or their practice nurses themselves. I would receive a tetchy letter from a GP from time to time because the specialist registrar in the Diabetes Review Clinic had not included all the blood-test results and other measures in detail in his/her letter to the GP (although they had, of course, all been measured in our clinic). The GP had not been in receipt of all the data they needed for their secretary to copy straight into their records and enable them to claim extra payment therefrom – although the letters would never admit that this was the reason they were complaining. The devolvement of care exclusively to general practice from specialist care has been railroaded through, despite it having long been recognised that patients with the condition require access to both GP and hospital-based specialist teams many times in their life. Referrals between the two should not only be seamless but dependent entirely on the need of the particular patient and independent of cost. Not to mention the issue of patient choice, which is conveniently ignored by those GPs determined to save money by refusing to refer their patients to hospital, if at all possible.

32

Listening to Such Rubbish

SOME YEARS AGO, PARI WAS EXPECTED, WITH ALL OTHER nurses in the National Health Service, to undergo the 'Agenda for Change' assessment. This process was spun by the government as being an exercise in assuring that all nursing roles were paid at the correct rate, the implication being that some nurses might even end up within a higher pay scale. I am not sure that I ever came across a nurse who had received an increase in her/his salary as a result of this review: I met many, however, who ended up being down-graded and receiving a lower salary. In my non-nursing view, the whole exercise ended up causing a lot of upset and the demoralisation of the army of professional, hard-working nurses, whose role was under-valued by the process, in both senses of the word.

Pari had been receiving one of the highest nursing pay scales in the hospital, and rightly so as far as I was concerned, in view of her experience, expertise and excellent leader-ship. When the result of her assessment came through, it put her on a lower scale, with a significant reduction in her status and salary band – both of which she had built up to and earned over many years. Pari was not going to take this lying down, and she fought the decision robustly, with my wholehearted support, going to a full appeal hearing, to which I accompanied her. The final result of all this was that justice, in her case at least, was done and her previous pay scale restored. Successful though the outcome was, the whole process, as far as I was concerned, was degrading and would have been completely unnecessary if only her most senior nursing and management colleagues had understood her worth to her patients and to the hospital trust itself.

Not so long after Pari retired and Sally took over as lead diabetes specialist nurse for the trust, she was faced with a similar situation. Yet another reorganisation of nursing and management roles in our trust effectively removed the position of lead diabetes specialist nurse, putting her job at risk. She was therefore faced with having to apply via a competitively interviewed process for a post with a management role which would at least preserve some of her previous clinical DSN duties. We were relieved that with my very strong support she was appointed to the role of 'clinical services manager for diabetes and endo-crinology'. That sounded very good, but the new role also included responsibility for managing other services, such as haematology, which she had neither the training for nor interest in. It also meant that she was drawn into other tedious nursing managerial roles that she definitely did not enjoy.

Sally did not tolerate fools gladly, very much like myself, although she usually dealt with them more politely than I did! And like me she said what she thought. Sometimes, I think, this put her at odds with a colleague who had not been pulling his or her weight; but that is what being a leader is all about. She was as passionate about promoting the cause of people with diabetes as Pari had been, and equally passionate about standing behind not only her DSN colleagues, but all members of the diabetes team. I soon learned how much I could trust her myself and we became very much on the same wavelength. I could always rely on her for support. For one thing, I could walk in to her office, put my feet on the desk and swear like a trooper about the most recent 'cock-up' that had occurred – usually, I have to say, involving the hospital management. Sally would laugh out loud in my face, but I always knew that she agreed with me and could be trusted unequivocally.

One morning Sally came into my office looking really miserable and almost in tears. 'What's the matter?' I asked her.

'Why do I have to spend time listening to such rubbish?!' she blurted out in reply.

'Tell me about it,' I said, indicating the seat next to me and inviting her to sit down.

'I've just spent the best part of an hour and a half sitting in on the daily board holders' meeting,' Sally explained. 'What a *complete* waste of time! They ramble on and on about how many beds are needed in areas of the hospital, about how few beds there are to go round and about the problem of the elderly people who are "medically fit" for discharge but have nowhere to go. All of these are things that they are not able to influence themselves, either way. It wouldn't be so bad if they were not all so self-important, if they didn't take the whole damn charade so seriously!' I knew where she was coming from. I could envisage the whole gaggle of nursing managers with their clipboards in hand discussing the issues at interminable length.

Unfortunately, management roles in our health service are generally paid more than clinical roles – when it patently should be the other way around – and a move into management is the only option available to many nurses to better their income. There should be a reversion to giving ward sisters/male charge nurses (*please* stop calling them 'ward managers') more status and a significantly higher pay scale in the process. Nurses who care for patients should be valued more, and paid more, than nurses who manage the process. But that is just my point of view. It was also the case, I knew very well, that both doctors and nurses who adopted management roles often inevitably seemed to lose their clinical common sense and 'sold out' to the management dictum: the need to save money at all costs, whatever the cost to clinical need and effectiveness.

'Can't you just tell them to "bugger off"?' I asked Sally.
'I've tried that!' she laughed at me.
'Or forget to turn up?'
'They'd soon notice my absence and insist that I go to the meetings regularly. It's such a lot of rubbish, and a waste

of time I could be spending on patient care and clinical issues.' I understood the dilemma she was in. Her post as lead DSN had been put at risk, threatening her with potential redundancy. We had supported her application to this alternative management role in order to protect some of her valuable clinical services at least. But in the process she was being expected to involve herself in a lot of time-wasting management bureaucracy. There was no easy option if we were not going to lose her completely. For the time being she was just going to have to carry on and 'grin and bear it'.

33

Listening Over the Years

MOST CONSULTANT PHYSICIANS DURING MY TIME HAD a contractual obligation to take part in the 'acute' on-call general medicine rota. This entailed being on call, together with our teams, for all the medical cases requiring emergency admission to hospital in the catchment populations which we served, which in the case of our hospital was around 300,000 people. It also meant that you were the consultant physician who was called if any advice was needed, either by a general practitioner from outside the hospital or about a medical or surgical patient in the hospital. In my case, for over a quarter of a century I would be on call roughly once a week for twenty-four hours, on a rota which included Friday morning to Saturday morning, as well as being 'post-take' for much of the Saturday – sorting out the emergency medical cases who had been admitted during the preceding twenty-four hours. In addition to this, I would also be on call for one weekend (from 9 a.m. Saturday to 9 a.m. Monday) every month.

At all other times of the week I still had to pursue my full-time ward round, outpatient clinic and teaching commitments. There was no compensatory time off following an on-call period, like some other specialties have the benefit of, such as anaesthetists, who operated with an on-off rota system. The work had to go on the next day. If I had been on call for a weekend, for example, I would have to start by about 8 a.m. on a Monday morning to see those general medicine patients admitted to the Medical Admissions Unit overnight on Sunday night, or still in A & E waiting for admission; this before conducting a full ward round on the twenty to forty patients already under my care on my base ward and outlying wards, with the aim of finishing on time to get to the Monday grand round by about 12.30 p.m. (which, as postgraduate clinical tutor for more than ten years, I had founded and had to chair) before arriving at the Diabetes Centre by 2 p.m. to start my diabetes new patient clinic, which usually would go on until about 6 p.m.

The acute medical on-call 'takes' never ceased to provide medical surprises. Unfortunately, they did not all end as happily as the tale of Jayne with pneumococcal septicaemia, which I told at the beginning of this story. One morning I was presented to another young woman of about the same age as Jayne on the Medical Admissions Unit. She had been admitted during the night as an emergency through the Accident and Emergency Department, unconscious and confused, thrashing around and resisting attempts for the doctors and nurses to examine her. She had been found in this state in a room in a sea-front hotel. The information available from the hotel was that she was visiting from Plymouth in the West Country and was staying in the hotel to attend some sort of computer course in Eastbourne. The A & E and medical doctors on the overnight shift had been unable to explain what was wrong with her, but they had a strong suspicion that the woman may have taken an overdose of drugs while alone in the hotel room. The tests on her blood and urine, however, had so far not identified any of the common substances that we come across following attempts at self-harm. I took a look at the woman myself, noting that she was still unconscious and agitated and rather flushed and red in the face, but that otherwise there was nothing abnormal to find on examining her or in the results of all the blood tests that had been taken.

While I was seeing other newly admitted patients on the Medical Admissions Unit, the woman's husband and his father-in-law arrived. They had driven together overnight all the way from Plymouth, her husband having heard the news of his wife's admission to hospital from the hotel. They were both red-eyed and exhausted. I took them in to the office to talk to them in private. I explained honestly that we had so far not been able to ascertain what was wrong with Margaret; for that was her name. Her husband Brian told me that his wife was normally fit and well and that she had had no previous health problems. They had a mentally disabled daughter, which was a burden for them both, but something that they had coped with together for many years. When I asked as tactfully as possible whether there was any reason why Margaret may have been under stress or depressed, enough perhaps to take an overdose with the aim of ending her life, Brian was clearly shocked by the suggestion. No, he told me. She had driven up to Eastbourne and was staying in the hotel alone, but she had been enjoying the computer course and had been fine when she had spoken to him on the phone the previous evening. She had been looking forward to coming home at the end of the week.

'One last thing,' I asked, as the two men got up to leave. 'It was reported to me that one of the ambulance men thought he could smell an unusual damp odour in her room when she was picked up unconscious. Did you notice this when you went to the hotel?'

'Oh no,' said Margaret's father. 'I have a very keen sense of smell and would certainly have picked up on any unusual smell if there had been one.' With that the husband and father went back to the hotel to catch up with their sleep after their long overnight journey.

During the day, Margaret gradually came round and by the evening she appeared to be back to normal. She seemed as bemused as we were as to the cause of her admission to our hospital. It was only the next day that I learnt that Margaret's husband Brian, having gone back to the hotel to sleep after his long overnight journey from the West Country, had later been found dead in bed in the same hotel room that his wife had occupied. The cause of his death was found to be carbon monoxide poisoning. It transpired that the hotel had recently had some new gas heaters installed. The engineer had apparently been at fault in incorrectly fitting the heater vents, causing fumes containing carbon monoxide to enter the room. I was devastated to think that I had followed but dismissed this possible line of enquiry; and the fact that I had been deflected by the reassurance from Margaret's father did not make me feel any better. I am sure he must have felt equally desolate at the loss of his son-in-law.

Fascinating though it was for much of the time, this burden of general medicine was the most tiring part of one's life. Not only did we admit the patients but we had to continue to care for them and treat them until their discharge or, occasionally, until another colleague in the relevant specialty could be persuaded to take over the patient's care, which might be never. My consultant colleague in diabetes and endocrinology and I were also on call every day to see patients who had been admitted with diabetes or an endo-crine problem. We would take over their care immediately, whichever ward they were on and whether or not we had a bed on our D & E ward to transfer them to. When referred a patient whose problem was their specialty, many of my other consultant colleagues would give some advice in the patient's notes but conclude with a statement like, 'I'll be happy to take over the patient's care when a bed becomes available on my ward.'

I had been part of the medical on-call rota for twenty-seven years, right up to my retirement at the age of sixty-five.

I would not have continued this gruelling rota for so long if I hadn't wanted to. But I knew that it took a toll not only on myself, but, more importantly, on my wife and children. All consultant physicians work very hard in today's health service and most have the same work ethic. For the people who choose this way of life it is just part of their nature to do so because of the professional satisfaction that it brings them. In later years, however, it was made more arduous by the knowledge that some groups of physicians, the cardiologists being the first, were bit by bit coming off the medical on-call rota, and therefore increasing the workload for those who were still left toiling at this particular coal face. The appointment of a couple of Medical Admissions Unit consultants, who did no out-of-hours work or weekend cover, had not significantly changed the degree of responsibility of this on-call commitment by the time I did retire.

I am not complaining in retrospect. I never looked for thanks from my peers, and especially not the hospital managers. But I have to say that, having arrived at my early sixties, I was struck dumb when my consultant physician colleague, who was the clinical director of medicine at the time (a management role), replied to my request to reduce my on-call commitments by saying, 'But I thought you enjoyed it, Jeremy.' He refused my request, even though he and I knew that in many hospitals it was not thought reasonable, or perhaps even safe, for consultant physicians to continue out-of-hours on-call rotas after a certain age. He never enquired as to why it was that I subsequently left him behind as my annual professional appraiser after meeting up with him every year for this reason over a good many years, and why I had found another colleague with whom I could relate to more easily to be my appraiser.

34

A Listening Specialty

THE PRACTICE OF DIABETES AND ENDOCRINOLOGY IS
mainly an outpatient specialty. We spend much of our time
in the endocrinology outpatient clinics and the Diabetes
Centre working to keep people out of hospital. Diabetes
care is all about helping people with the condition to understand and control their diabetes as well as they can, thereby
enabling them to keep fit and healthy and free of the nasty
potential complications of the disease, if possible. People
with diabetes generally feel well, not ill. You would not know
they have a health problem and that is how we try to keep
it. It is for this reason that, having raised the money to build
and equip our District Diabetes Centre, we were determined
to make it a welcoming place to visit and somewhere that
would feel more like a hotel than a hospital. I remember
well a trip Pari Sheppard, my first DSN, and I made to a
well-known furniture store, jumping on and off arm chairs
and sofas to test them for comfort until we decided which
range to go for. There was to be no question of plastic hospital chairs in *our* lounge area, even if what we chose did

cost considerably more at the outset! 'It's all about getting rid of the pyjama and dressing gown approach to diabetes care,' I used to say.

In addition to the several scheduled clinics going on every day of the week, the Diabetes Centre was also open for the whole week to anybody wanting to call in for help and advice. You did not need to have an appointment if your problem was urgent – although we did ask you to phone in advance, if possible, to tell us you were coming in with your foot problem, or whatever, so that we had time to get your records ready for your visit. You would always be seen by somebody. And a lot of the work of the centre was done on the phone, talking to people about how their diabetes was going, reassuring patients with diabetes and their family members, and so on. There was also always much work to be done educating and supporting other health-care professionals who would telephone asking for advice about how to manage a patient, including GPs and practice and district nurses. We would have liked to have had the man- and woman-power to keep the centre open at weekends as well, but we didn't. Pari and I did, however, establish a weekly 'young adult' evening clinic for teenagers and young adults with diabetes, meaning that they could attend the Diabetes Centre without having to take time off work or college.

The fact is that the 1.5 million people in the UK with diabetes are normal people (whatever that is!) and consider themselves to be so. They are people like you and me, who just happen to have diabetes. Unfortunately, the lack of a clear understanding in the general population about what sort of a condition diabetes is, frequently gives rise to discrimination – in employment, insurance, driving, schooling and many other ways socially. There are not many jobs people with diabetes are not able to do these days, however, and I illustrate this by referring to the fact that we had a number of insulin-treated active firefighters in the area on our books. This is an occupation which requires all its members to have a high degree of general physical fitness. It is also a job which entails entering smoke-filled rooms while wearing breathing apparatus and one in which the lives of your colleagues, as well as your own, can be put at risk if you are not fully fit. If you also have diabetes, you cannot afford to have a problem – such as a 'hypo' (low blood sugar) attack – during the job. As a consequence, these firefighters with insulin-treated diabetes always made a special effort to keep their diabetes under careful control.

Yes, people with diabetes may need admission to hospital if something goes wrong, such as a heart attack or the development of a foot infection. And because diabetes is such a common disease, something like twenty per cent of all people in hospital at any one time have diabetes, whatever they have been admitted for – including elective surgery and childbirth. The task of catching up with all these people with diabetes in hospital is enormous, and something that in our hospital, like most others, we were aware we were only able to succeed in doing on a 'firefighting' basis: in spite of requesting that our colleagues let us know about any patient admitted under their care with diabetes, so that we could give them help and support with their diabetes while they were an inpatient, this did not always happen and we often found out about inpatients with diabetes by chance or if we were called because something had gone awry with their diabetes control.

Similarly, endocrinology involves the diagnosis, treatment and care of people with diseases of the endocrine (hormone producing) glands. These include disorders of the thyroid gland (which in themselves are about as common as diabetes), and diseases of the adrenal gland (such as Addison's disease), the pituitary gland (including pituitary tumours and pituitary failure) and the sex-hormone glands (those of the ovaries and testes which can lead to reproductive problems). Many of these conditions, once treated and stabilised, require following up for the rest of a person's life if they are to remain well, and people with conditions such as Addison's disease and pituitary diseases are given annual follow-up appointments indefinitely at a minimum.

I should say that this accepted 'best practice' follow-up approach to people with endocrine disorders has in recent times been repeatedly questioned by primary care trusts and others looking to reduce the numbers of patients attending 'secondary' (actually, 'specialist') clinics in hospital, and therefore the costs involved. This approach has been encapsulated in recent years by a crusade to drill down on a consultant's 'new to follow-up clinic ratio'. The question asked:

'Why do these patients need to continue to be followed up in "secondary" (specialist) care?' The answer: 'Because they have conditions which primary-care doctors are not trained in or equipped to deal with.' I would find the suggestion that I was for some reason giving repeat appointments to patients who did not need them profoundly offensive: 'Do they think I am providing this service for myself rather than for my patients?! That I have so much spare time that I would not discharge any patient who did not really need to come back!!' I would cry out frequently in my frustration with the enemies of good practice.

We did bring patients with endocrine problems up to the hospital for special tests, but these were almost all conducted with the patient as a day case, and therefore they usually did not require admission to hospital overnight. That in itself had become more and more difficult over the years. We might book a patient to come in for an endocrine day test, only to find that the wards were full and that there was not a single bed available for the patient to have the test in. The test would therefore have to be postponed and rearranged for a later date, which would hopefully not meet with the same problem of bed unavailability the following time. This was a situation which was frustrating for us, but more so for the patient – who had perhaps arranged a day off work or extra childcare for this reason – and which ultimately led to a delay in conducting these tests which were essential for arriving at a correct diagnosis of an endocrine condition and subsequently commencing its treatment. The simple

solution would have been to allow us a metabolic investigation room, which would be reserved for these patients
requiring endocrine tests. Unfortunately, try as hard as we
might, we were never given the space and the small amount
of money that it would have required to set such a facility up.

35

Listening at the End

AT ANY ONE TIME, IN ADDITION TO ALL MY OUTPATIENT clinics and Diabetes Centre patients, I would also have somewhere between twenty and thirty medical inpatients under my care. Many of these would be elderly patients who had been admitted as an emergency on the acute general medical take, but who had remained in hospital after the younger patients had been treated, got better and gone home. Sometimes the elderly patients did have pneumonias or 'mini' strokes or whatever, but often the reason for their continued hospital stay was that they were just too old or too frail to be discharged home safely again on their own and sat waiting for 'placement', which usually meant some type of care home, either for temporary convalescence or on a permanent basis.

The hospital managers often referred to these patients as 'bed blockers', a horrible and undignified label as far as I was concerned, even if it was true that their presence in an acute medical bed was an inappropriate use of resources. But the old people could not help the fact that they had ended up there, and it was not a nice place for them to be either. Many of them had some degree of dementia, which meant that they tended to be disorientated and frightened in hospital, their confusion being made very much worse as a result of these unfamiliar surroundings. There has been much discussion in the media recently about the need for better and more appropriate care for these old people, and especially about the lack of joined-up thinking in dealing with their social needs. But this is not a new problem. In my experience, the problem has been going on for many years without adequate redress: it is just that, with the enormous demands and economic pressures on our National Health Service, the politicians have only now got hold of the issue. The fact was that in our hospital we had no dedicated specialised geriatric service to cope with all those who were old and in need of specialist support, which was a disgrace.

Even though I had had no formal specialist training in geriatric medicine, I always did my best to treat the elderly patients with respect and to insist that my junior medical and nursing colleagues treated them likewise when they were under our care waiting for an appropriate placement. I always made a point of asking an elderly lady or gentleman whom I met on my ward round for the first time about their life history. It is incredible what you find out from elderly people if you do this. How the old man fought his way through Normandy after landing on the D-Day beaches, or how the old lady worked in the land army in the same war or had travelled as a governess to the Indian subcontinent before it. The people I spoke to had had every sort of job you could imagine. There were the miners and painters and decorators, the carpenters and plumbers, as well as the teachers and vicars and members of parliament. Yes, and writers and doctors as well. My junior doctor colleagues probably thought I was rambling on ('He's reminiscing again!'), but I didn't care. I never looked over my shoulder to check whether they were interested or not. I would say to my team directly as we left the bay, 'What a fascinating and interesting old man/woman!'

As I moved into my sixties, I started to become aware of the hard fact of ageism myself. And that didn't just mean the ageism coming from those superficial drug representatives who implied to the rest of my team during lunchtime meetings that I was 'out of date and past it' – this because I was not ready to endorse their particular new drug until I had become satisfied that the agent was indeed effective and safe enough for me to start prescribing to my own patients, something my early training in pharmacology had taught me was vital. Younger consultant colleagues were understandably ambitious and certainly hardworking, making important contributions to their side of the service. But, more unhappily, I learnt early on that such younger colleagues' ambition often centred more on their own progress than that of the service. Even more unpalatably, I discovered that some of the younger men were not averse to manoeuvring behind my back with managers and other colleagues, even stooping to bad-mouth the service I had founded and indeed myself.

These days, hospital doctors are required to ask all patients under their care about their preferences with respect to what is crudely termed their 'resuscitation status'. I never had a problem discussing this issue with my patients, but at the same time was always adamant that it was not my wish to impose myself in an unkindly way on any elderly patient who was too confused and frightened to understand what it was they were being asked. In any case, information which might be gained in this way from a confused patient does not constitute 'informed consent', does it? As I neared my own retirement I became increasingly more sensitive to this view.

'Well, Dorothy,' I said to a frail, little old lady with pneumonia whom I came across on my last ward round. She may have been very ill and very frail but I could see that she was mentally as bright as a button. 'How do you feel about us trying to resuscitate you if your heart were to stop and your breathing give out?' She gave me the most beautiful smile in reply: 'I've had a good life, haven't I? I don't want any of that, and I certainly would *never* want to be put on an artificial breathing machine!' She squeezed my hand, wanting to reassure me. 'But thank you for asking, doctor,' she said, most politely. I walked away from her bed and remained deep in thought as I walked the long hospital corridors towards the exit for the last time. I hope there is a doctor around to listen to me when my time comes.

Acknowledgements

I am grateful for the fantastic support I received from all the members of my team, the doctors, nurses and many others with whom I worked over all those years; for the love and support of my wife and family, who found me difficult to live with as a result during many of them; and, last but not least, of course, to my patients themselves.

Thank you to Cressida Downing for her helpful advice with the first draft of the manuscript. Thank you also to the team at Quartet Books: to the chairman Naim Attallah for believing in the project from the start and to Peter Jacobs, my editor, for his expert professional help.

I do not proffer *A Listening Doctor* to my reading audience as evidence that I am in any way an expert in the art and science of listening. Indeed, I am aware that there have been many times in my career when I have been deficient by not listening attentively or carefully enough to my patients, some of whom have criticised me for this fact, either at the time or after. I do, however, commend the art (and science) of listening to my colleagues – the doctors of the present and future – as a skill which should be preserved at all costs, if possible, whatever other directions medicine might take us in the twenty-first century.

Notes

Chapter 6 'Bring Back the Four-Letter Word' was first published in the *Association of British Clinical Diabetologists' Newsletter*, 9 (2004), 4.

Chapter 25 'Listening Together' is an edited version of: Bending, J. J., Kingswood, J. C., 'Joint Diabetes Renal Clinics are "Best Practice"', *British Journal of Diabetes & Vascular Disease*, 7 (2007), 202.

Chapter 26 'Listening to Complaints' and Chapter 27 'Listening to Another Complaint' contain an edited version of the article: Bending, J. J., Foster, A. V. M., 'Litigation and the Diabetic Foot', *Practical Diabetes International*, 2/1 (2004), 19–23.

Chapter 28 'Listening to the Candidates' includes an edited version of the article: Bending, J. J., 'The GP Letter', which appeared in *A Concise History of the MRCP Examination: Celebrating 150 Years*, The Royal College of Physicians of London (2009).

Chapter 28 'Listening to the Candidates' also contains extracts from the 'History of The Royal College of Physicians of London' on their website. When I contacted the RCP Library asking for any references they might have referring to 'listening doctors', they replied that they were not familiar with the term and could find no references to the term in their collections as well as in national and international catalogues. They reiterated that the distinguishing term for physicians up until the nineteenth century was 'doctor' and for surgeons 'Mr', because historically physicians came from an academic background whereas surgeons came from an apprentice trade.

Chapter 30 'Divide and Rule' and Chapter 33 'A Listening Specialty' contain sections of the chapter: Bending, J. J., Keen, H., 'Organisation of Care: The Diabetes Care Centre – A Focus for More Effective Diabetes Treatment and Prevention', in Alberti, K. G. M. M., DeFronzo, R. A., Keen, H., Zimmet, P., ed., *International Textbook of Diabetes* (John Wiley & Sons Ltd, 1992), 1593–1600.